Spin-Spin Splitting
in NMR Spectra

An Introduction

to the

Analysis of

Spin-Spin Splitting

in High-Resolution

Nuclear Magnetic

Resonance Spectra

JOHN D. ROBERTS, *California Institute of Technology*

W. A. Benjamin, Inc., New York, 1962

AN INTRODUCTION TO THE ANALYSIS OF SPIN-SPIN
SPLITTING IN HIGH-RESOLUTION NUCLEAR MAGNETIC
RESONANCE SPECTRA

Manufactured in the United States of America
Library of Congress Catalog Card Number: 61-12990

First printing, July 1961.
Second printing, with corrections,
January 1963.

The publisher is pleased to acknowledge the assistance
of Ann Van Der Vliet, who edited the manuscript;
Betty Binns, who designed the book and dust jacket;
and Felix Cooper, who produced the illustrations.

W. A. BENJAMIN, INC.
2465 BROADWAY, NEW YORK 25, NEW YORK

TO learn to apply the methods of wave mechanics in a practical way seems to involve a quantum-like transition with a relatively low transition probability. Chemistry students by the thousands are exposed to the principles and jargon of wave mechanics and are able to talk in a most knowing way about orbitals, overlap, spin, etc. But very few of these students can set about to make any sort of an actual calculation of resonance energies of conjugated systems or the energy levels of nuclear spin systems, and this despite the fact that the mathematics involved, although perhaps tedious, usually does not require more than college algebra.

I lay the blame for this situation just as much on the writers in the field and the students themselves as on the intrinsic difficulties of the subject. Many writers seem sincerely anxious to impart their knowledge to novices but may have forgotten, or never really knew, how difficult it is for the average chemist to make the transition between knowing and not knowing. Certainly, it is a long and tedious job to try to make clear in writing step by step what is involved, particularly when exciting prospects of discussing applications and new developments beckon. Students in their turn make things hard for themselves by their failure to work problems or to work through even simple derivations.

Although it may seem presumptuous to some readers for a synthetic organic chemist to write an introduction to the quantum mechanical formulation of nuclear spin states and transitions, I have pointed out elsewhere [*J. Am. Chem. Soc.*, **82,** 5767 (1960)] that I believe all chemists can use nuclear magnetic resonance spectroscopy with greater interest, skill, and understanding by having at least a rudimentary knowledge of the quantitative theory of spin-spin splitting. The purpose of this book is to show that the path to making practical calculations of spin-spin splittings is not really difficult. No prior knowledge of quantum mechanics or the mathematics thereof will be assumed. Familiarity with the elements of nuclear magnetic resonance spectroscopy at the level of Roberts, "Nuclear Magnetic Resonance," McGraw-Hill Book Company, Inc., New York, 1959, and Jackman, "Applications of Nuclear Magnetic Resonance Spectroscopy in Organic Chemistry," Pergamon Press, New York, 1959, will be particularly important. Since in my opinion it is very difficult to gain mastery of the material presented without a great deal of practice, exercises have been interspersed at appropriate places in the text. It is strongly recommended that these be worked through as encountered.

The coverage throughout is intended to be illustrative rather than comprehensive. The AX and AB cases are discussed in considerable detail to show how the nuclear spin states are formulated, their energies computed, and the probabilities of transitions between them calculated. Then AX_2 and AB_2 are compared in sufficient detail to make clear how more lines can appear than would be expected from a simple counting of the number of interactions involved. Some discussion is presented of ABX to illustrate the important point that a nucleus such as X can often appear to be coupled to A even when J_{AX} is zero. The effect of changing the relative signs of coupling constants is also considered in connection with ABX. Finally the A_2X_2 systems with $J_{AX} \neq J'_{AX}$ are covered to show that it is possible to have spectra influenced by J_{AA} and J_{XX} even when $(\nu_A - \nu_X) \gg J_{AA}$ or J_{XX}.

No discussion will be presented of the many advantages of applying group theory to the problem of simplifying the formulation of complex spin states having some degree of symmetry. There are several reasons for this: First, many less-familiar mathematical operations would have had to be introduced and explained. Second, the use of group theory is most important as a mathematical shortcut and does not contribute in itself in an important way to an understanding of the principles of spin-spin splitting. Finally, the need for mathematical shortcuts has been much reduced by the availability of computer programs for calculation of transition energies and intensities for even quite complex spin systems.

I am deeply indebted to Professor Harden M. McConnell for helping me through his very important contribution to the field [H. M. McConnell, A. D. McLean, and C. A. Reilly, *J. Chem. Phys.*, **23**, 1152 (1955)]; this book is very largely based on an impromptu private lecture that Professor McConnell delivered on July 4, 1956. I am also much indebted to Dr. V. Schomaker for many hours of patient explanation of quantum mechanical principles. The success (if any) of the treatment is largely due to these gentlemen; the shortcomings and errors are all my own.

Many helpful suggestions regarding the manuscript were received from Dr. Marjorie C. Caserio, Professor Max T. Rogers, and Dr. Thomas H. Regan. The NMR spectra were obtained with skill and patience by Mr. Donald R. Davis, and the manuscript was prepared by Mrs. Allene Luke and Miss Joy Matsumoto.

The heretofore unpublished research described in this book was supported by the Office of Naval Research.

JOHN D. ROBERTS

Contents

Spin-Spin Splitting
in NMR Spectra

chapter one

Introduction. Nuclear Magnetic Resonance Absorption

THE PROTONS of organic molecules in the liquid state may give very simple or very complex patterns of nuclear magnetic resonance (NMR) absorption lines. In general, the complexity of NMR spectra is determined by the numbers of protons in chemically different locations in the molecule, the magnetic "spin-spin" interactions between reasonably contiguous protons, and the rates of exchange between protons in the various locations.[1] In many instances, spin-spin splitting of resonance lines is an especially complicating factor; some knowledge of the underlying theory is essential to intelligent divining of structural features through analysis of line multiplicities and intensities.

The currently favored procedure for the analysis of spin-spin splitting was developed by McConnell, McLean, and Reilly[2] and considerably extended by others.[3-5] Unfortunately, the language of presentation has been that of the molecular spectroscopist, so the ideas are not easily accessible to organic chemists, who are in fact by far the most important potential users of the theory.

It is the purpose of this book to present a simplified theory of spin-spin splitting for nuclei of spin 1/2 in the hope of providing (1) an introduction to more definitive treatments [3-5] and (2) a sound theoretical basis for use of more descriptive approaches.[1,6] Use of some concepts and mathematics of quantum mechanics will be inevitable, but these will be explained in so far as is possible in language familiar to organic chemists. At the outset, a simple picture of nuclear resonance absorption will be given that differs in emphasis from the one offered previously[1] in being more useful for understanding spin-spin splitting than for understanding the operation of an NMR spectrometer.

1-1 Nuclear magnetic resonance absorption

Many atomic nuclei act like charged spinning bodies, the circulation of charge producing a magnetic moment along the axis of rotation. Certain nuclei of particular interest to organic chemists—^{1}H, ^{13}C, ^{15}N, and ^{19}F—are classified as having spin I of 1/2. This means that the magnitude of their magnetic moments in any given direction has only two equal, but opposite, observable values that correspond to spin quantum numbers equal to $+1/2$ and $-1/2$. Thus, if the nuclei are immersed in a magnetic field taken as the z direction, they can only be regarded as being effectively lined up with the field ($I_z = -1/2$) * or against the field ($I_z = +1/2$). As with compass needles in the earth's magnetic field, the more favorable energy state is the one corresponding to alignment with the field. Of course, the difference in energy between the states ΔE is expected to be proportional to the strength of the applied field H at the nucleus and is equal to $\gamma \hbar H$, where $\hbar$ is Planck's constant h divided by 2π and γ is a proportionality constant typical of each variety of nucleus (^{1}H, ^{13}C, ^{15}N, etc.).[1,3]

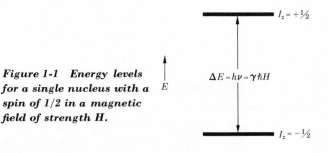

Figure 1-1   Energy levels for a single nucleus with a spin of 1/2 in a magnetic field of strength H.

Obviously, we can in principle adjust the energy difference between the states with I_z $+1/2$ and $-1/2$ to any desired value by suitably adjusting H; however, at ordinary

* The assignment of $I_z = -1/2$ for the more favorable energy state is used here, but not earlier,[1] and corresponds to taking H in the *negative* z direction in conformity with Pople, Schneider, and Bernstein.[3]

temperatures, within the practically attainable range of values for H, the equilibrium concentrations of nuclei in the two possible states are always very nearly equal. This is because the energy differences between the states are quite small and because alignment of the nuclei with the field is opposed by thermal agitation in accord with Boltzmann's law.[1]

In NMR spectroscopy, as with other kinds of spectroscopy involving absorption of electromagnetic radiation, the energy change ΔE associated with a given transition, as for a proton from $-1/2$ to $+1/2$ (Figure 1-1), is related to the frequency ν of the radiation by $\Delta E = h\nu$. Since $\Delta E = \gamma \hbar H$, we see that $\nu = \gamma H/2\pi$.

To observe a nuclear resonance transition (assuming it is of the type classified as "allowed"), we have to adjust either the frequency ν of the radiation or the strength of the magnetic field at the nucleus H until $\nu = \gamma H/2\pi$. Experimentally, it is most convenient to hold ν constant and to vary H continuously with time until (and beyond) the point where resonance (energy absorption) occurs. In principle,

Figure 1-2   Schematic diagram of a simple nuclear magnetic resonance spectrometer.

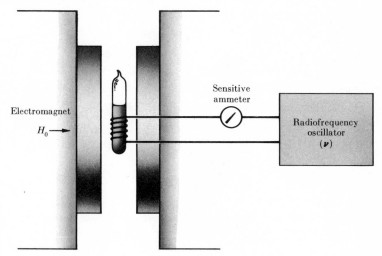

Electromagnet

$H_0 \longrightarrow$

Sensitive
ammeter

Radiofrequency
oscillator
(ν)

3

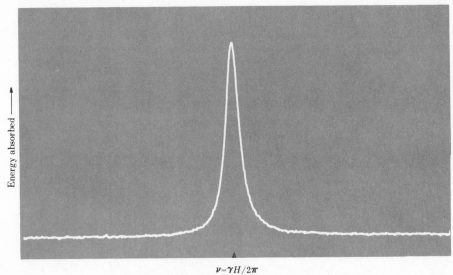

$\nu = \gamma H/2\pi$

$H_0 \longrightarrow$

Figure 1-3   Typical energy absorption curve as a function of magnetic field H.

resonance can be observed by a device as simple as the one shown in Figure 1-2. Here, ν is the frequency of an oscillator (customarily radio frequency rf), which bathes the sample in electromagnetic radiation, and H_0 is the strength of the applied magnetic field. When the field at the nuclei H reaches the point where ν is equal or very close to $\gamma H/2\pi$, energy is absorbed. The current flow from the oscillator will then increase and can be detected by the ammeter in series with the oscillator coil. Further increase of H will eventually make $\nu \ll \gamma H/2\pi$, and the current will then decrease to its original value. In practice the form of the energy absorption curve as a function of H appears as shown in Figure 1-3, that is, the peak is centered on the point at which $\nu = \gamma H/2\pi$.

1-2   Chemical shifts

Differences in absorption-line positions for nuclei of the same kind, such as protons or ^{19}F, but located in different molec-

4

ular environments, are called *chemical shifts*.[7] The magnitude of a given chemical shift is always taken in practice with reference to a standard. For protons the customary standard was originally the resonance-line position of the protons of water used as an *external* reference. Currently, tetramethylsilane is the favored standard substance; it is mixed with the sample to provide an *internal* proton reference line.[8] Chemical shifts have their origin in diamagnetic and paramagnetic shielding effects [3] produced by circulation of both bonding and nonbonding electrons in the neighborhood of the nuclei. These effects are strictly proportional to the magnitude of the applied field H_0 so that, for any H_0, the chemical shift $\delta_{AB}H_0$ between two nuclei A and B can be expressed by the following equation, where σ_A and σ_B are the shielding proportionality constants characteristic of each nuclei:

$$\delta_{AB}H_0 = \sigma_A H_0 - \sigma_B H_0 = (\sigma_A - \sigma_B)H_0 \qquad (1\text{-}1)$$

The chemical-shift parameter δ_{AB} is particularly useful for reporting differences in resonance-line positions because not all spectrometers operate at the same values of the magnetic field H_0. In practice it turns out to be very convenient to measure resonance-peak separations in units of cycles per second (cps). If frequency units are used and two peaks as for A and B are separated by n cps, then

$$\delta_{AB} = n/\nu$$

where ν is the oscillator frequency. Normally, δ values are computed with reference to a standard. Extensive tables of δ values relative to various standards are available for protons, ^{19}F, ^{13}C, ^{14}N, ^{17}O, etc., in a variety of typical molecules.[3, 6]

For a given proton spectrum, the areas under resonance peaks are rather closely proportional to the number of each kind of proton involved. Thus, the spectrum of ethyl alcohol shows three groups of peaks, which have areas in the ratio

1:2:3. These groups can be shown by isotopic substitution or by comparison of the spectrum with those of other alcohols to correspond to the resonances of the —OH, —CH$_2$—, and —CH$_3$ protons, respectively. Such measurements of relative peak areas have obvious utility in qualitative and quantitative analysis.

Comparisons of peak heights in place of comparisons of peak areas can give very erroneous results if the peaks do not have the same shapes. In general, resonance-line shapes are functions of many variables, and it is not uncommon for the peaks of a given sample to have quite different shapes.[9]

EXERCISE 1-1

Figure 1-4 shows a 60-Mc proton spectrum of diacetone alcohol in a raw form, the peaks being measured in cycles per second with tetramethylsilane as an internal standard. Calculate δ values for each peak relative to tetramethylsilane and also τ values where τ (in ppm) is defined[8] as $10 - [\text{chemical shift from } (CH_3)_4Si \text{ (cps)/oscillator frequency (cps)}] \times 10^6$. Iden-

Figure 1-4   Spectrum at 60 Mc of diacetone alcohol with tetramethylsilane as internal standard.

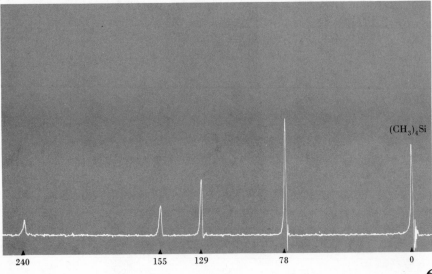

240   155   129   78   0

6

tify the protons of the molecule that are responsible for each peak by making rough comparisons of peak areas and available data for other molecules.[1,6]

1-3   Spin-spin splitting—qualitative theory

Many organic molecules with protons on contiguous carbon atoms, such as ethyl derivatives CH_3—CH_2X (X $\neq$ H), show principal groups of proton resonance lines as they correspond to chemical shifts; but each group has a considerable fine structure that results from "spin-spin splitting." [10] Taking as a typical example the protons of an ethyl group as in ethyl iodide, the chemical-shift difference between the methyl and methylene protons gives two groups of lines (see Figure 1-5); these are split ("first-order" effect) into

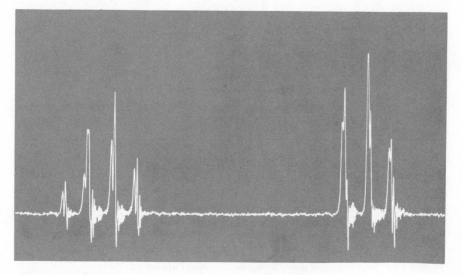

Figure 1-5   Nuclear resonance spectrum of ethyl iodide at 60 Mc.

three and four lines, respectively, by spin-spin interactions. Several of the lines of the three-four pattern are further discernibly split as the result of what is called "second-order" spin-spin splitting. The chemical shift is easily recognized

7

as such by the fact that the spacing between the main groups is directly proportional to H_0, the applied magnetic field. In contrast, the first-order splitting is field-invariant (at least when the chemical shift is large) and, for this reason, is easily recognizable also. The second-order splitting is field-dependent for reasons to be explained later; it will not be discussed further at this time.

EXERCISE 1-2

The spectrum of acetaldehyde dimethyl acetal shown in Figure 1-6 was taken at 60 Mc with reference to tetramethylsilane. Compute the position of each of the lines at 30 Mc.

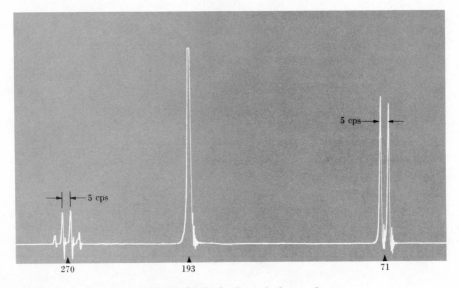

Figure 1-6   Spectrum of acetaldehyde dimethyl acetal at 60 Mc with tetramethylsilane as internal reference.

The first-order splitting is independent of the applied field because it arises from fixed increments in the total magnetic field produced at a given nucleus by the magnetic moments of neighboring nuclei and transmitted by the bonding electrons.[1,3] Consider a nucleus undergoing resonance

8

absorption that has a single neighboring proton. The effective magnetic field at the absorbing nucleus will have one of two possible values, depending upon whether or not the magnetic quantum number I_z of the adjacent proton is $+1/2$ or $-1/2$. The field of the proton thus either augments or decreases the applied field of the magnet. Since nuclear magnetic moments are independent of the applied field, the effect of the proton on the resonance absorption-line position will be independent of the applied field.

It is easy to demonstrate by isotopic substitution that the three-four pattern of lines for the spin-spin splitting of typical ethyl groups arises from the interaction of each group of protons with the other. Deuterons have much smaller magnetic moments than protons. Substitution of one deuteron on each methyl of an ethyl compound gives a triplet resonance for the methylene group (somewhat broadened because of the small magnetic effect of the deuteron), whereas substitution of two deuterons gives a doublet resonance with the splitting being due to the remaining proton. Thus, for this particularly simple case, the multiplicity of lines is $(n + 1)$, where n is the number of protons on the contiguous carbons. A number of similar examples are discussed elsewhere.[1, 3, 6] That the methylene resonance of an ethyl group is not complicated beyond the observed quartet by the interaction of the magnetic effect of one of the methylene protons on the other will be given considerable attention later. For the present, we shall only note that chemically equivalent protons do not normally show spin-spin splitting. Thus, only single proton resonance lines are observed for H_2, CH_4, C_6H_6, etc.

In general, the effect of one proton on the resonance of of another proton or group of equivalent protons depends on the number and kind of intervening chemical bonds and on the stereochemical relationships of the interacting groups. Normally, we expect splittings for nonequivalent protons in saturated systems to be approximately 15 cps when located on the same carbon, 5 to 8 cps when located on contiguous carbons, and essentially zero when separated by more than two carbons. Where restricted rotation or unsaturated groups are involved, widely divergent splittings are often observed.[1, 3, 6, 11, 12]

The ratios of the line intensities in spin-spin splitting patterns usually follow simple rules [13] when the chemical shifts are large with respect to the splittings. Further attention will be given later to the resonance-line intensities associated with spin-spin splitting.

EXERCISE 1-3

Sketch out approximately the proton spectra to be expected at 60 Mc for each of the following substances: (a) methyl ethyl ether, (b) 1-chloro-1-iodoethylene, (c) isobutylene, (d) fluoroform, and (e) acetophenone diethyl acetal.[14]

EXERCISE 1-4

The spectra shown in Figure 1-7 are for single pure substances (except as noted) and for the most part were taken at room temperature. The proton spectra were taken at 60 Mc, and the chemical shifts are in cps from $(CH_3)_4Si$ as internal reference. The fluorine spectra were taken at 56.4 Mc.

Deduce a structure for each unknown from its spectrum and molecular formula. It is suggested, in so far as possible, that each of the important lines or groups of lines be accounted for.

Values of δ in units of parts per million and based on water as a reference standard [1, 3] can be converted approximately to τ values based on tetramethylsilane [6, 8] by adding 5.2.

The problems are arranged approximately in order of difficulty of interpretation. The reasons for some of the spin-spin splittings shown may become clear only after considerable further study. It may be helpful to review the answers to these problems as the work on each of the later chapters is completed.

*Introduction.
Nuclear
Magnetic
Resonance
Absorption*

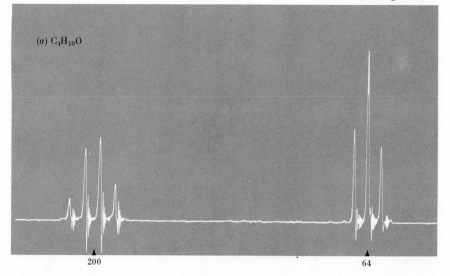

(a) $C_4H_{10}O$

200   64

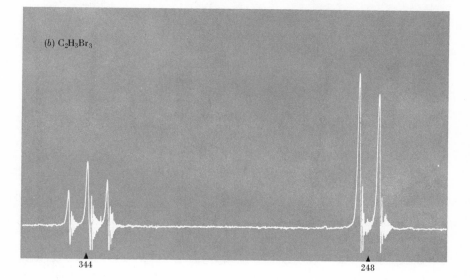

(b) $C_2H_3Br_3$

344   248

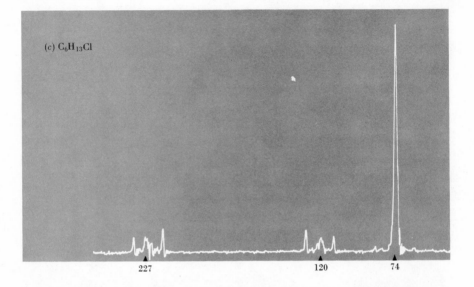

(c) $C_6H_{13}Cl$

227   120   74

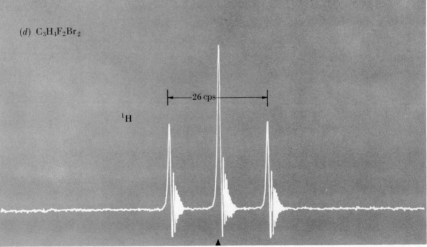

(d) $C_3H_1F_2Br_2$

^1H

|←—26 cps—→|

275

12

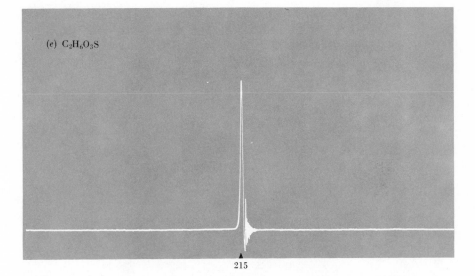

(e) $C_2H_6O_3S$

215

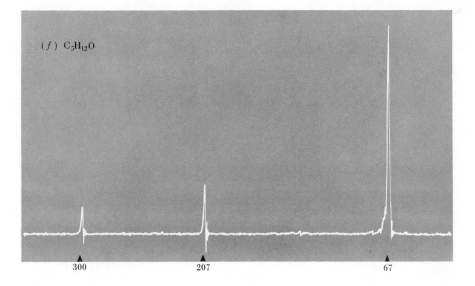

(f) $C_5H_{12}O$

300   207   67

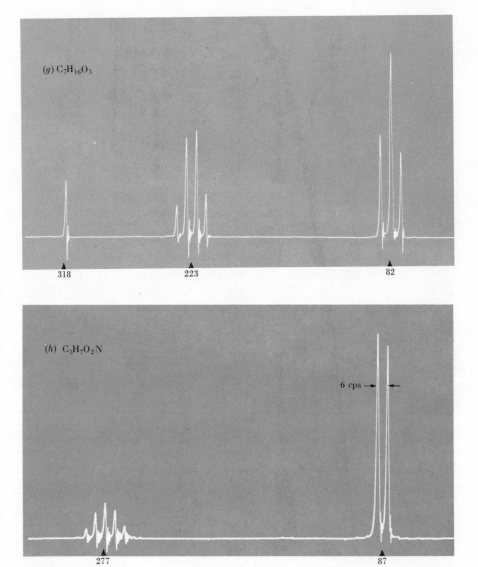

(g) $C_7H_{16}O_3$

318   223   82

(h) $C_3H_7O_2N$

6 cps

277   87

14

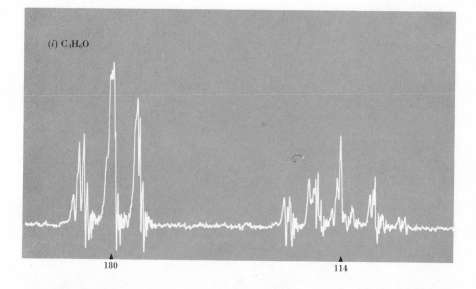

(*i*) C_4H_6O

180   114

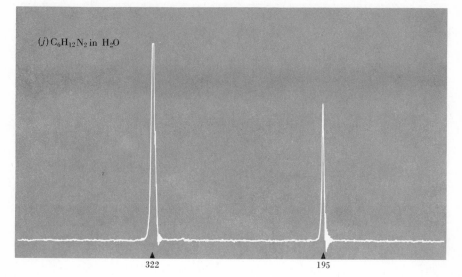

(*j*) $C_6H_{12}N_2$ in H_2O

322   195

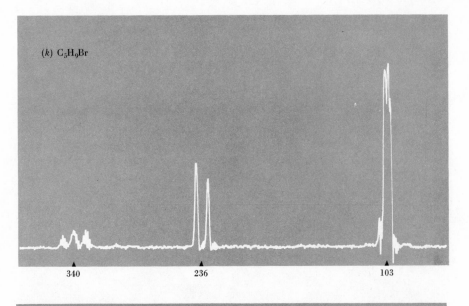

(k) C_5H_9Br

340   236   103

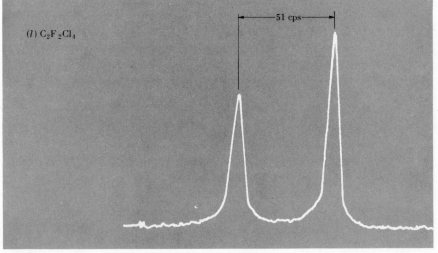

51 cps

(l) $C_2F_2Cl_4$

16

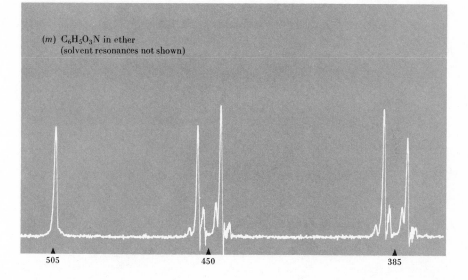

(*m*) $C_6H_5O_3N$ in ether
(solvent resonances not shown)

505   450   385

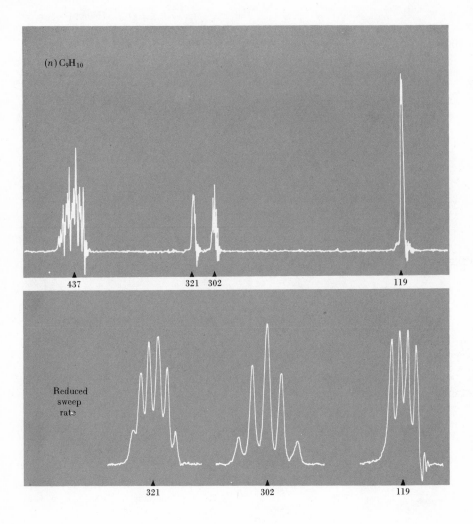

$(n)\,C_9H_{10}$

437   321 302   119

Reduced
sweep
rate

321   302   119

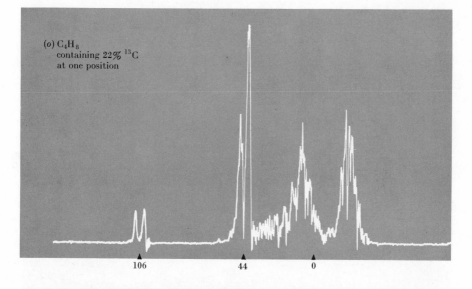

(*o*) C_4H_8
containing 22% ^{13}C
at one position

106   44   0

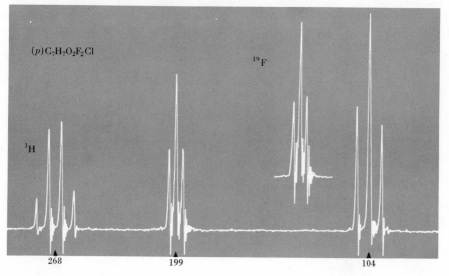

(*p*) $C_7H_7O_2F_2Cl$

^{19}F

^1H

268   199   104

19

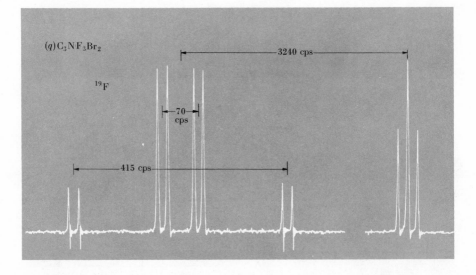

(q) $C_3NF_3Br_2$

^{19}F

3240 cps

70 cps

415 cps

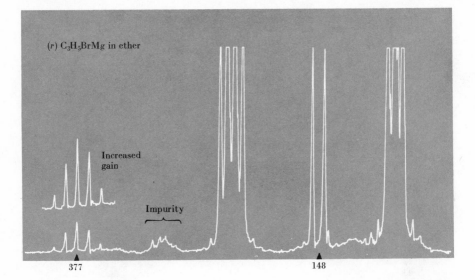

(r) C_3H_5BrMg in ether

Increased gain

Impurity

377   148

20

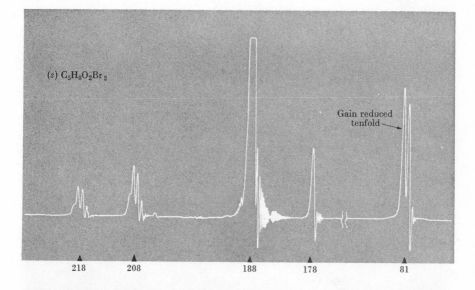

(s) $C_5H_8O_2Br_2$

Gain reduced tenfold

218   208   188   178   81

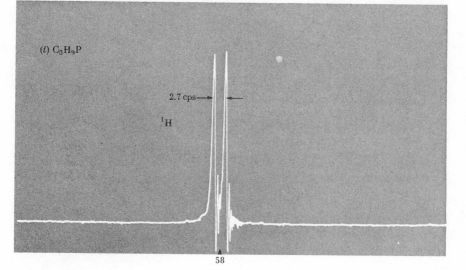

(t) C_3H_9P

2.7 cps

^1H

58

21

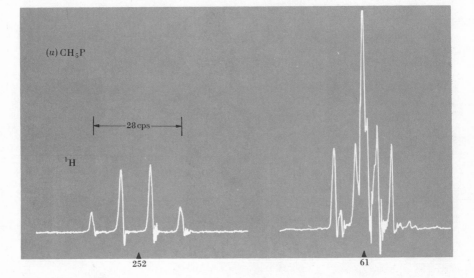

$(u)\,CH_5P$

^1H

$\longmapsto$ 28 cps $\longrightarrow$

▲
252

▲
61

22

References

1. An elementary introduction to this subject is available in J. D. Roberts, "Nuclear Magnetic Resonance. Applications to Problems in Organic Chemistry," McGraw-Hill Book Company, Inc., New York, 1959.
2. H. M. McConnell, A. D. McLean, and C. A. Reilly, *J. Chem. Phys.*, **23**, 1152 (1955).
3. J. A. Pople, W. G. Schneider, and H. J. Bernstein, "High-resolution Nuclear Magnetic Resonance," McGraw-Hill Book Company, Inc., New York, 1959, Chap. 6.
4. E. B. Wilson, Jr., *J. Chem. Phys.*, **27**, 60 (1957).
5. P. L. Corio, *Chem. Revs.*, **60**, 363 (1960).
6. L. M. Jackman, "Applications of Nuclear Magnetic Resonance Spectroscopy in Organic Chemistry," Pergamon Press, New York, 1959.
7. W. G. Proctor and F. C. Yu, *Phys. Rev.*, **77**, 717 (1950); W. C. Dickinson, *Phys. Rev.*, **77**, 736 (1950); G. Lindström, *Phys. Rev.*, **78**, 817 (1950); H. A. Thomas, *Phys. Rev.*, **80**, 901 (1950).
8. G. V. D. Tiers, *J. Phys. Chem.*, **62**, 1151 (1958).
9. See Ref. 1, particularly pp. 78, 85, and 103.
10. H. S. Gutowsky, D. W. McCall, and C. P. Slichter, *Phys. Rev.*, **84**, 589 (1951); E. L. Hahn and D. E. Maxwell, *Phys. Rev.*, **84**, 1246 (1951).
11. D. R. Davis, R. P. Lutz, and J. D. Roberts, *J. Am. Chem. Soc.*, **83**, 246 (1961).
12. R. R. Frazer, *Can. J. Chem.*, **38**, 549 (1960); J. H. Richards and W. F. Beach, *J. Org. Chem.*, **26**, 623 (1961).
13. Ref. 1, Chap. 3.
14. P. R. Shafer, D. R. Davis, M. Vogel, K. Nagarajan, and J. D. Roberts, *Proc. Natl. Acad. Sci. U.S.*, **47**, 49 (1961).

Introduction.
Nuclear
Magnetic
Resonance
Absorption

*Quantum
Mechanical
Treatment
of Spin-Spin
Interaction
between
Two Nuclei*

chapter two

IT turns out that the theoretical treatment of spin-spin interactions between two nonequivalent nuclei of spin 1/2 is much simpler when the spin interaction J is small compared to the chemical-shift difference $\delta_{AB}H_0$ than when J is comparable to or larger than $\delta_{AB}H_0$. Following the usual convention,[1] we shall designate the former case for two nuclei as an AX situation and the latter as an AB situation. This sort of classification is quite generally useful because the mathematical treatments of the members of each class are closely related. Thus, analysis of a particular A_2B_3X system (one group of two equivalent magnetic nuclei A_2, coupled to a second group of three equivalent nuclei B_3, with an interaction constant J_{AB} comparable to $\delta_{AB}H_0$, and either or both groups A_2 and B_3 coupled to an additional nucleus X so that $\delta_{AX}H_0$ and $\delta_{BX}H_0$ are much larger than J_{AX} or J_{BX}; for example, CH_3CH_2F at low H_0 values) will be useful for all such systems.

EXERCISE 2-1

Classify each of the following molecules as to the character of spin system it presents (such as AB_2X, etc.), noting that ^{12}C and ^{16}O have no magnetic moments, ^{19}F has a spin of $1/2$, and Cl acts as though it has no magnetic moment: (*a*) CH_2O, (*b*) CH_3F, (*c*) $CH_3CH_2CH_3$, (*d*) $CH_2=CHCl$, (*e*) $CH_2=CF_2$, (*f*) C_6H_5F, and (*g*) *o*-chlorofluorobenzene.

2-1   Qualitative treatment of the AX *system*

The coupling constant J_{AX} for an AX system will almost always be small compared with the chemical shift $\delta_{AX}H_0$ when two different nuclei, such as hydrogen and fluorine, are involved. Typical AX cases of this sort are H—F,

HC≡CF, HCCl$_2$F (chlorine acts as a nonmagnetic nucleus [2]), HCCl$_2$CCl$_2$F, etc. If we were to use the treatment outlined in Chapter 1, we would rationalize the spin-spin splitting that occurs for these molecules in terms of the effect of the magnetic moment of one nucleus on the magnetic field at the other nucleus. However, it is more convenient and precise to analyze the over-all energy levels of the AX system. In the first place, we note that there are four possible magnetic states that correspond to the four possible combinations of the spin quantum numbers of A and X (see Table 2-1). Now, if the energy change associated with A going from $I_z = -1/2$ to $I_z = +1/2$ is larger than that for X, the order of the states as given is the same as the order of the energies. Assuming for the moment no spin-spin interaction between A and X, we have the energy diagram shown in Figure 2-1. There are two A transitions (4 → 2,

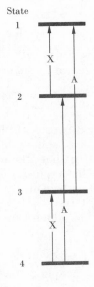

Figure 2-1   Energy levels for a two-spin system. The numbering of the states corresponds to that used in Table 2-1.

3 → 1) and two X transitions (4 → 3, 2 → 1) in which F_z, the sum of $I_z(A)$ and $I_z(X)$, changes by one unit, which is a necessary condition for an *allowed* transition. The man-

ner of predicting whether or not a transition is allowed will be discussed more fully later; for the present it will suffice to note that, by the stated criterion, the transitions $4 \to 1$ and $3 \to 2$ are *not* allowed transitions.

In the absence of spin-spin interaction the nuclei behave independently of one another; therefore, ΔE_A for $4 \to 2$ will be equal to $3 \to 1$, and ΔE_X for $4 \to 3$ will be equal to $2 \to 1$. The observed resonance spectrum for the system will then consist of just two lines, the $4 \to 2$, $3 \to 1$, A

Table 2-1   Magnetic States of an AX System

State	$I_z(A)$	$I_z(X)$	$I_z(A) + I_z(X) = F_z$
1	$+1/2$	$+1/2$	$+1$
2	$+1/2$	$-1/2$	0
3	$-1/2$	$+1/2$	0
4	$-1/2$	$-1/2$	-1

transitions occurring together at low field, and the $4 \to 3$, $2 \to 1$, X transitions occurring together at high field (see Figure 2-2).

Now if spin-spin interaction occurs, we have to modify the energy-level diagram to take account of the differences in energy that depend on whether or not $I_z(A)$ and $I_z(X)$ have

Figure 2-2   Schematic spectrum for an AX system in the absence of spin-spin interaction. The transitions are numbered to correspond to the changes in state shown in Figure 2-1.

A

$4 \to 2$
$3 \to 1$

X

$4 \to 3$
$2 \to 1$

Increasing $H \longrightarrow$
(ν = constant)

the same or opposite signs. The normal expectation is that
if $I_z(A)$ and $I_z(X)$ have the same sign (unpaired spins),
A and X will interact so that this alignment will be less
stable, have more energy, than if $I_z(A)$ and $I_z(X)$ have opposite signs.* Therefore, states 1 and 4 will be pushed up in
energy by spin-spin interaction while states 2 and 3 will be
stabilized. The energy changes for each pair of states will
be equal but opposite in sign. If we let $\pm J/4$ be the change
in energy for each state as the result of spin-spin interaction, our energy diagram is changed as shown in Figure
2-3.

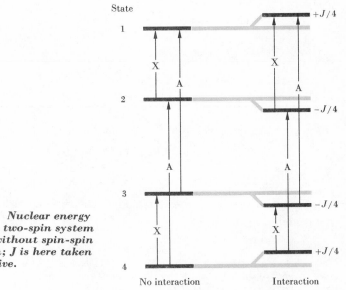

*Figure 2-3 Nuclear energy
levels for a two-spin system
with and without spin-spin
interaction; J is here taken
to be positive.*

Now, we see that the A transition $(4 \rightarrow 2)$ has decreased
in energy by $J/2$ while $3 \rightarrow 1$ has increased in energy by
$J/2$. Similarly, the X transition $(4 \rightarrow 3)$ has decreased in
energy by $J/2$ while $2 \rightarrow 1$ has increased by $J/2$. The spectrum will thus show two A lines, each separated by $J/2$ from
the position where resonance would occur in the absence of

* In some circumstances the interaction has the opposite effect on
the energy, but this does not change the results in the AX case.

spin-spin interaction. The total separation of the A lines will of course be J. Nothing that has been taken into account so far would lead one to predict that the two A transitions would have other than equal probability. A demonstration that this is actually the case will be made later.

The positions and relative intensities of the X transitions $(4 \rightarrow 3, 2 \rightarrow 1)$ can be assigned exactly as for the A transitions. The predicted spectrum is shown in Figure 2-4.

EXERCISE 2-2

Extract J_{AX} and δ_{AX} from the 60-Mc AX spectrum shown in Figure 2-5.

EXERCISE 2-3

The nuclear moment of ^{13}C is much smaller than that of the proton. Would you expect if one were to use a constant oscillator frequency ν that the resonance of ^{13}C would come at a lower or higher magnetic field than that of ^{1}H? Explain.

EXERCISE 2-4

Consider the effect on the energy levels and transitions of the AX system of having J negative instead of positive.

Figure 2-4 Schematic spectrum for an AX system having spin-spin interaction. The chemical shift has to be quite large with respect to J to have equal probabilities for each of the pairs of transitions, as shown.

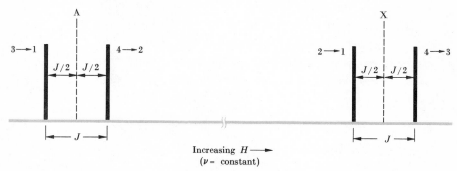

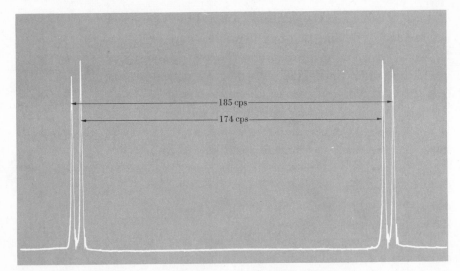

Figure 2-5   The nuclear resonance spectrum of an AX *system at 60 Mc.*

2-2   *Qualitative and quantitative treatment of the* A_2 *system*
Our understanding of the AB system will be considerably facilitated if we first consider spin-spin interaction between two equivalent nuclei of an A_2 system such as H_2.

It will be desirable at this point to introduce suitable wave functions for describing the magnetic states of individual nuclei and systems of nuclei. Throughout we shall consider only nuclei of spin 1/2 for which $I_z = \pm 1/2$ and for such nuclei, taken as individuals, but two wave functions α and β will be required. We shall assign each nucleus with $I_z = +1/2$ the spin wave function α; and each with $I_z = -1/2$ the spin wave function β. Since we shall be interested only in stationary states of our nuclear systems, i.e., states that do not change with time except through intervention of some external agency, we can write the following equation for the energy corresponding to a given wave function for a single nucleus: [3]

$$\mathcal{H}\alpha = E\alpha \tag{2-1}$$

where $\mathcal{H}$ is the Hamiltonian energy operator, α is the spin wave function, and E is the energy of the nucleus in the applied magnetic field.

The properties of α are taken to be such that Equation (2-2) holds where ϕ refers to the spin variable and $d\phi$ may be regarded as a differential increment of spin space, the integration being over all possible angles of rotation of the spin:

$$\int \alpha^2 \, d\phi = 1 \tag{2-2}$$

Spin wave functions that meet this condition are said to be "normalized." We shall use only normalized spin wave functions henceforth.

Equation (2-2) may be regarded as being closely analogous to the familiar equation (2-3) for normalized electronic wave functions where the integration is over all space: [4]

$$\int_{-\infty}^{\infty} \psi^2 \, d\tau = 1 \tag{2-3}$$

Another condition we shall put on our wave functions α and β for a given nucleus is that they be "orthogonal." This means that a given nucleus cannot have I_z values of $+1/2$ and $-1/2$ at the same time. Mathematically stated,

$$\int \alpha(1)\beta(1) \, d\phi = 0 \tag{2-4}$$

where (1) is an index number that indicates that the wave functions α and β both refer to the particular nucleus (1).

Since a wave function such as α is a function of the coordinate ϕ, it is convenient to recast the energy equation and integrate with respect to ϕ from 0 to 360° so as to eliminate the coordinate.* Thus,

$$\mathcal{H}\alpha = E\alpha$$
$$\alpha\mathcal{H}\alpha = E\alpha^2$$
$$\int \alpha\mathcal{H}\alpha \, d\phi = E\int \alpha^2 \, d\phi \tag{2-5}$$
$$E = \int \alpha\mathcal{H}\alpha \, d\phi / \int \alpha^2 \, d\phi$$
$$= \int \alpha\mathcal{H}\alpha \, d\phi \text{ if } \alpha \text{ is normalized; i.e., } \int \alpha^2 \, d\phi = 1$$

* The procedure here is quite analogous to that used for electronic wave functions.[5]

We are now face to face with the problem of evaluating $\mathcal{H}$. For a single nucleus, we know that $E = \gamma\hbar H/2$ when $I_z = +1/2$ and that $E = -\gamma\hbar H/2$ when $I_z = -1/2$. This permits us to write $\mathcal{H}$ in the form $\gamma\hbar H I_z$. Thus, for the single nucleus with $I_z = +1/2$,

$$E = \int \alpha(1)\mathcal{H}_1\alpha(1)\,d\phi$$

and because $\mathcal{H}_1$ is here a constant we can write

$$E = (\gamma\hbar H/2)\int \alpha(1)\alpha(1)\,d\phi$$

$$= \gamma\hbar H/2 \text{ since by the normalization condition } \int \alpha(1)\alpha(1)\,d\phi = 1 \quad (2\text{-}6)$$

where, as before, (1) is the index number for reference to a particular nucleus. The energy E is in ergs if γ has the usual units of radians per gauss per second and H is in gauss. It is more convenient in most practical NMR work to have E in units of cycles per second, so we shall henceforth use $\varkappa$ in place of $\gamma\hbar$, and let $\varkappa$ have the units cycles per second per gauss.

If account is taken of nuclear shielding, Equation (2-6) then becomes

$$E = (\varkappa/2)(1 - \sigma_1)H_0 \quad\quad\quad (2\text{-}7)$$

where H_0 is the applied field and σ_1 is the shielding parameter for nucleus (1).

Now we consider two nuclei, both with $I_z = +1/2$, and with negligible interaction between them (i.e., $J = 0$), so that their energies E_1 and E_2 can be computed separately:

$$\mathcal{H}_1\alpha(1) = E_1\alpha(1)$$
$$\mathcal{H}_2\alpha(2) = E_2\alpha(2)$$

The wave function ψ for two nuclei considered simultaneously is the product function (2-8).

$$\psi = \alpha(1)\alpha(2) \quad\quad\quad (2\text{-}8)$$

The energy operator $\mathcal{H}$ for ψ is then the sum of the separate operators $\mathcal{H}_1$ and $\mathcal{H}_2$.

$$\mathcal{H} = \mathcal{H}_1 + \mathcal{H}_2 \quad\quad\quad (2\text{-}9)$$

We can show that ψ and $\mathfrak{H}$ give the proper energy E for the system which, if the nuclei do not interact, is of course just the sum of E_1 and E_2.

$$E = \int \psi \mathfrak{H} \psi \, d\phi / \int \psi^2 \, d\phi$$

$$= \int \alpha(1)\alpha(2)(\mathfrak{H}_1 + \mathfrak{H}_2)\alpha(1)\alpha(2) \, d\phi / \int [\alpha(1)\alpha(2)]^2 \, d\phi \qquad (2\text{-}10)$$

Noting that $\mathfrak{H}_1$ does not operate on $\alpha(2)$ nor $\mathfrak{H}_2$ on $\alpha(1)$, that the denominator of Equation (2-10) is unity because the wave functions are normalized, and that there is a separate variable ϕ for each spin, the energy is given by

$$E = \int \alpha(1)\mathfrak{H}_1\alpha(1) \, d\phi \int [\alpha(2)]^2 \, d\phi + \int \alpha(2)\mathfrak{H}_2\alpha(2) \, d\phi \int [\alpha(1)]^2 \, d\phi$$

$$= E_1 + E_2$$

which with the aid of Equation (2-7) becomes

$$E = (\gamma_1/2)(1 - \sigma_1)H_0 + (\gamma_2/2)(1 - \sigma_2)H_0$$

$$= (\gamma/2)H_0(2 - \sigma_1 - \sigma_2) \text{ if } \gamma_1 = \gamma_2 = \gamma$$

$$= \gamma H_0(1 - \sigma) \text{ if } \sigma_1 = \sigma_2 = \sigma \qquad (2\text{-}11)$$

EXERCISE 2-5

Write the stationary-state product functions for each of the states of the AX system discussed in Section 2-1, and calculate their energies, neglecting spin-spin interaction, with the aid of Equation (2-10). Let $\gamma_A = \gamma_X$, but note that $\sigma_A \neq \sigma_X$. Also calculate the transition energies for all the possible transitions between the states.

If our two nuclei undergo spin-spin interaction with one another, we include an interaction operator $\mathfrak{H}_{12}$ in Equation (2-9) so that

$$E = \int \alpha(1)\alpha(2)[\mathfrak{H}_1 + \mathfrak{H}_2 + \mathfrak{H}_{12}]\alpha(1)\alpha(2) \, d\phi \qquad (2\text{-}12)$$

The form of $\mathfrak{H}_{12}$ will be discussed a little later.

With two equivalent nuclei, a fresh complication arises for those states having F_z [i.e., $I_z(1) + I_z(2)$] equal to zero. The two product wave functions $\alpha(1)\beta(2)$ and $\beta(1)\alpha(2)$ would seem to suffice to describe the possible states. However,

33

these wave functions are not proper ones because they violate a principle of nature—it is impossible to designate which of the members of an equivalent pair of nuclei has $I_z = +1/2$ and which $-1/2$. The problem does not arise for $\alpha(1)\alpha(2)$ because here both nuclei have the same spin. We must find functions to describe such states as $\alpha(1)\beta(2)$, which permit us to interchange the nuclei without doing more than changing the sign of the wave function. There are two independent ways of doing this.* The possible wave functions are

$$(1/\sqrt{2})[\alpha(1)\beta(2) + \beta(1)\alpha(2)] \quad \text{and} \quad (1/\sqrt{2})[\alpha(1)\beta(2) - \beta(1)\alpha(2)]$$

$$(2\text{-}13)$$

The first of these functions is unchanged when the index numbers of the nuclei are interchanged, (1) for (2) and (2) for (1). This is called a *symmetric* wave function.

The second function changes sign when the index numbers are interchanged and is called an *antisymmetric* function.

Each of these functions requires the coefficient $1/\sqrt{2}$ so that it will be properly normalized. Thus,

$$\int \{(1/\sqrt{2})[\alpha(1)\beta(2) + \beta(1)\alpha(2)]\}^2 \, d\phi$$
$$= (1/2)\{\int [\alpha(1)\beta(2)]^2 \, d\phi + 2\int \alpha(1)\beta(2)\beta(1)\alpha(2) \, d\phi + \int [\beta(1)\alpha(2)]^2 \, d\phi\}$$

$$(2\text{-}14)$$

Invoking the "orthogonality" condition, Equation (2-4), we know that

$$\int \alpha(1)\beta(1) \, d\phi = \int \beta(2)\alpha(2) \, d\phi = 0$$

and hence that Equation (2-14) reduces to

$$(1/2)\{[1] + 2[0] + [1]\} = 1$$

EXERCISE 2-6

Verify that $(1/\sqrt{2})[\alpha(1)\beta(2) - \beta(1)\alpha(2)]$ is a normalized wave function.

* The same problem arises with electrons and is discussed very clearly in Chap. IV of Ref. 3.

Quantum
Mechanical
Treatment
of Spin-Spin
Interaction
between
Two Nuclei

EXERCISE 2-7

Compute a normalization factor [analogous to the factor $1/\sqrt{2}$ in Equations (2-13)] for $[\alpha(1)\alpha(2)\beta(3) + \alpha(1)\,\beta(2)\alpha(3) + \beta(1)\alpha(2)\alpha(3)]$.

EXERCISE 2-8

Show that the two wave functions of Equations (2-13) are orthogonal.

EXERCISE 2-9

Show that $\alpha(1)\alpha(2)$ and $(1/\sqrt{2})[\alpha(1)\beta(2) - \beta(1)\alpha(2)]$ are orthogonal functions.

In the absence of spin-spin interaction, i.e., $\mathcal{3C}_{12}$ of Equation (2-12) equals zero (or $J = 0$), we find that the energies corresponding to the symmetric and antisymmetric wave functions are equal. For the symmetric function, we can compute the energy as follows:

$$E = \int(1/\sqrt{2})[\alpha(1)\beta(2)+\beta(1)\alpha(2)][\mathcal{3C}_1+\mathcal{3C}_2](1/\sqrt{2})[\alpha(1)\beta(2)+\beta(1)\alpha(2)]\,d\phi$$
$$= (1/2)\int[\alpha(1)\mathcal{3C}_1\alpha(1) + \beta(1)\mathcal{3C}_1\beta(1) + \alpha(2)\mathcal{3C}_2\alpha(2) + \beta(2)\mathcal{3C}_2\beta(2)]\,d\phi$$
$$= E_1 - E_1 + E_2 - E_2 = 0 \tag{2-15}$$

That the energy is zero shows that there is no net magnetic interaction between an applied field and two equivalent nuclei when F_z and $\mathcal{3C}_{12}$ equal zero.

EXERCISE 2-10

Compute the energy of the antisymmetric state corresponding to the wave function $(1\sqrt{2})[\alpha(1)\beta(2) - \beta(1)\alpha(2)]$ when $\mathcal{3C}_{12} = 0$.

The product function $\beta(1)\beta(2)$ describes the two-nucleus system when I_z for each is $-1/2$. Its energy can be evaluated as for $\alpha(1)\alpha(2)$ [see Equations (2-8) to (2-11)]:

$$E = \int\beta(1)\beta(2)[\mathcal{3C}_1 + \mathcal{3C}_2]\beta(1)\beta(2)\,d\phi$$
$$= -\gamma(1 - \sigma)H_0 \tag{2-16}$$

Table 2-2 Energy Levels and Transitions for Two Noninteracting Equivalent Magnetic Nuclei (A_2, $J = 0$)

F_z	Energy	Symmetric wave functions	Symbol*	Symbol*	Antisymmetric wave functions
$+1$	$+\gamma(1-\sigma)H_0$	$\alpha(1)\alpha(2)$	s_1		
0	0	$(1/\sqrt{2})[\alpha(1)\beta(2) + \beta(1)\alpha(2)]$	s_0	a_0	$(1/\sqrt{2})[\alpha(1)\beta(2) - \beta(1)\alpha(2)]$
-1	$-\gamma(1-\sigma)H_0$	$\beta(1)\beta(2)$	s_{-1}		

* The subscript corresponds to F_z.

36

Both the functions $\beta(1)\beta(2)$ and $\alpha(1)\alpha(2)$ are of course symmetric wave functions. The energy levels for two equivalent nuclei with no magnetic interaction are shown in Table 2-2. It is easy to see that all the transitions where the change in $F_z = \pm 1$ have the same energy and that this system of nuclei would give rise to only one resonance line. We shall show later that the transitions represented by the dashed arrows in Table 2-2 ($s_{-1} \rightarrow a_0$ and $a_0 \rightarrow s_1$) are forbidden.

Now, to save time and space, we shall introduce a number of very effective abbreviations, which, however, must be used with care if mistakes are to be avoided. In case of doubt, it may be best to write out the functions as we have done above. First, we shall abbreviate $\alpha(1)\beta(2)\alpha(3)\beta(4) \cdots$ as $\alpha\beta\alpha\beta \cdots$. The order will always be understood to be (1), (2), (3), etc. Next, we shall abbreviate the integrations in the following style:

$$\int [\alpha(1)\alpha(2)]^2 \, d\phi = \langle \alpha(1)\alpha(2) | \alpha(1)\alpha(2) \rangle = \langle \alpha\alpha | \alpha\alpha \rangle \tag{2-17}$$

The enclosing marks $\langle$ and $\rangle$ represent $\int \cdots d\phi$ and the vertical line here takes the place of the multiplication sign. The sequence of spin symbols on the right side of the vertical line will be understood to have a set of index numbers starting from one, whether these are written in or not. By convention, we shall have

$$| \alpha(\alpha\beta + \beta\alpha) \rangle = | \alpha(1)[\alpha(2)\beta(3) + \beta(2)\alpha(3)] \rangle = | \alpha\alpha\beta + \alpha\beta\alpha \rangle$$

and

$$| (\alpha\beta + \beta\alpha)(\alpha\beta + \beta\alpha) \rangle = | [\alpha(1)\beta(2) + \beta(1)\alpha(2)][\alpha(3)\beta(4) + \beta(3)\alpha(4)] \rangle$$
$$= | \alpha\beta\alpha\beta + \beta\alpha\alpha\beta + \alpha\beta\beta\alpha + \beta\alpha\beta\alpha \rangle$$

Integrals containing $\mathcal{H}$ or other operators will be abbreviated as follows:

$$\int \alpha(1)\alpha(2)(\mathcal{H}_1 + \mathcal{H}_2)\alpha(1)\alpha(2) \, d\phi = \langle \alpha(1)\alpha(2) | \mathcal{H}_1 + \mathcal{H}_2 | \alpha(1)\alpha(2) \rangle$$
$$= \langle \alpha\alpha | \mathcal{H}_1 + \mathcal{H}_2 | \alpha\alpha \rangle$$

EXERCISE 2-11

Evaluate each of the following integrals for nuclei with the same γ and σ: (a) $\langle \alpha \,|\, \mathcal{K}_1 \,|\, \beta \rangle$, (b) $\langle \alpha\alpha \,|\, \alpha\alpha \rangle$, (c) $\langle \alpha\alpha \,|\, \beta\alpha \rangle$, (d) $\langle (1/\sqrt{2})(\alpha\beta + \beta\alpha) \,|\, \mathcal{K}_1 \,|\, \alpha\beta \rangle$, (e) $\langle \beta\beta\alpha \,|\, \alpha\beta\beta \rangle$, (f) $(1/2) \langle (\alpha\beta - \beta\alpha) \,|\, \mathcal{K}_1 \,|\, (\beta\alpha + \alpha\beta) \rangle$, (g) $\langle \alpha\alpha\beta \,|\, \mathcal{K}_1 + \mathcal{K}_2 + \mathcal{K}_3 \,|\, \alpha\alpha\beta \rangle$, (h) $\langle \alpha\alpha\alpha \,|\, \mathcal{K}_1 + \mathcal{K}_2 + \mathcal{K}_3 \,|\, (1/\sqrt{2})\beta(\alpha\beta - \beta\alpha) \rangle$, and (i) $(1/4)\langle (\alpha\beta - \beta\alpha)(\alpha\beta + \beta\alpha) \,|\, (\alpha\beta + \beta\alpha)(\alpha\beta - \beta\alpha) \rangle$.

There are two remaining problems with regard to the A_2 case. One is to compute the change in energy levels when account is taken of spin-spin interaction, and the other is to calculate the transition probabilities. Of these, the transition-probability problem is the simpler; and, if we consider it first, we shall be able to complete our discussion of A_2 with negligible spin-spin interaction.

In computing transition probabilities, we are interested only in relative probabilities since, in practical work, we measure intensities of lines relative to one another at constant oscillator power and magnetic field using nuclei of the same type. Suppose we wish to determine the transition probability of $\beta\beta \rightarrow (1/\sqrt{2}) (\alpha\beta + \beta\alpha)$ relative to $\beta\beta \rightarrow (1/\sqrt{2}) (\alpha\beta - \beta\alpha)$. The relative probability for the first of these changes is proportional to

$$[\langle (1/\sqrt{2})(\alpha\beta + \beta\alpha) \,|\, F_+ \,|\, \beta\beta \rangle]^2 \qquad (2\text{-}18)$$

The rationale of Equation (2-18) is as follows: First, F_+ is a "raising" operator. We need a "raising" operator because the wave function $\beta\beta$ represents a lower energy state than $(\alpha\beta + \beta\alpha)$, and an increase in F_z is involved. The operation is carried out on $\beta\beta$ because we are considering $\beta\beta \rightarrow (1/\sqrt{2}) (\alpha\beta + \beta\alpha)$. If we wished to go the other way, the transition probability would be proportional to

$$[\langle \beta\beta \,|\, F_- \,|\, (1/\sqrt{2})(\alpha\beta + \beta\alpha) \rangle]^2 \qquad (2\text{-}19)$$

where F_- is a "lowering" operator.

The operations symbolized by F_+ (or F_-) are simple. With F_+, we go through the wave function and successively *raise* each nuclear wave function to the higher-energy spin state. If it is already at the highest spin state, F_+ makes the term equal to *zero*. The following operations of F_+ are typical:

$$F_+|\beta\rangle = |\alpha\rangle \tag{2-20}$$
$$F_+|\alpha\rangle = 0 \tag{2-21}$$

and

$$F_+|\beta\beta\rangle = |\alpha\beta\rangle + |\beta\alpha\rangle \tag{2-22}$$
$$F_+|\alpha\beta\rangle = 0 + |\alpha\alpha\rangle \tag{2-23}$$
$$F_+|\beta\alpha\rangle = |\alpha\alpha\rangle + 0 \tag{2-24}$$
$$F_+|\alpha\alpha\rangle = 0 \tag{2-25}$$

From this we see that if a single nucleus has the wave function α the energy cannot be *raised* to a higher value:

$$[\langle\alpha|F_+|\alpha\rangle]^2 = [\langle\alpha|0\rangle]^2 = 0$$

And, further, the change $\beta \to \alpha$ has unit probability:

$$[\langle\alpha|F_+|\beta\rangle]^2 = [\langle\alpha|\alpha\rangle]^2 = 1$$

EXERCISE 2-12

Evaluate each of the following terms: (a) $F_+|\alpha\beta\alpha\rangle$, (b) $F_-|(1/\sqrt{2})(\alpha\beta - \beta\alpha)$, (c) $F_+|(1\sqrt{2})\alpha(\alpha\beta + \beta\alpha)\rangle$, and (d) $F_+|(1/2)(\alpha\beta + \beta\alpha)(\alpha\beta - \beta\alpha)\rangle$.

For the change $\beta\beta \to (1/\sqrt{2})(\alpha\beta + \beta\alpha)$:

$$\begin{aligned}
[\langle(1/\sqrt{2})(\alpha\beta + \beta\alpha)|F_+|\beta\beta\rangle]^2 &= (1/2)[\langle(\alpha\beta + \beta\alpha)|(\alpha\beta + \beta\alpha)\rangle]^2 \\
&= (1/2)[\langle\alpha\beta|\alpha\beta\rangle + \langle\alpha\beta|\beta\alpha\rangle \\
&\quad + \langle\beta\alpha|\alpha\beta\rangle + \langle\beta\alpha|\beta\alpha\rangle]^2 \\
&= (1/2)[1 + 0 + 0 + 1]^2 = 2 \tag{2-26}
\end{aligned}$$

The significance of 2 as the answer will be considered later. For the moment it is more important to note that the raising operator F_+ serves to change $\beta\beta$ to a function that is identical (in the particular case) to the wave function of the upper state. Since the raised function is nonorthogonal to the upper-state function, the relative transition probability therefore is high. If the raised function were completely orthogonal to the upper-state function, the probability would be zero. Intermediate degrees of orthogonality are expected to give intermediate transition probabilities. In other words, the more the raised function "resembles" the upper-state function, the more probable the transition.

For $\beta\beta \rightarrow (1/\sqrt{2})(\alpha\beta - \beta\alpha)$, a *symmetric-to-antisymmetric transition*, the calculated transition probability is zero:

$$[\langle(1/\sqrt{2})(\alpha\beta - \beta\alpha)|F_+|\beta\beta\rangle]^2 = (1/2)[\langle(\alpha\beta - \beta\alpha)|(\alpha\beta + \beta\alpha)\rangle]^2$$
$$= (1/2)[1 - 1]^2 = 0 \tag{2-27}$$

It can be shown similarly that the probability for $(1/\sqrt{2})$ $(\alpha\beta - \beta\alpha) \rightarrow \alpha\alpha$ is also zero. Thus, as stated before, $s_{-1} \rightarrow a_0$ and $a_0 \rightarrow s_1$ are forbidden transitions. This means that when nuclear resonance absorption is observed for H_2, those molecules that have their nuclei in the a_0 state are predicted *not* to undergo resonance absorption at all! Indeed, the nuclei of molecules in the a_0 state (*para* hydrogen) should not undergo a change in magnetic quantum number unless the H—H bond is broken and they get reshuffled so as to go into one of the s states (*ortho* hydrogen).

EXERCISE 2-13

Evaluate the following terms: (a) $[\langle\beta\beta|F_-|\alpha\alpha\rangle]^2$, (b) $[\langle\alpha\alpha|F_+|(1\sqrt{2})(\alpha\beta + \beta\alpha)\rangle]^2$, (c) $[\langle\beta\beta|F_+|(1/\sqrt{2})$ $(\alpha\beta - \beta\alpha)\rangle]^2$, and (d) $[\langle\alpha\alpha\alpha|F_+|\alpha\beta\alpha\rangle]^2$.

EXERCISE 2-14

Calculate the probabilities for each of the AX transitions found in Exercise 2-5.

Nature conspires in an interesting way to disguise the fact that not all the molecules of H_2 undergo resonance absorption. There are three s states and one a state; and at equilibrium at ordinary temperatures in the absence of a very powerful magnetic field, 75 per cent of the molecules are s or *ortho* hydrogen. The nuclei of two-thirds of 75 per cent (or 50 per cent) of these molecules can make upward transitions. But these upward transitions have been shown already to have a relative probability of 2. The net probability is therefore unity.

For two hydrogens of the AX variety, there will be four possible upward transitions, each of which can be made by one-fourth of the molecules. Each of these transitions has unit probability. Consequently, the total relative transition probability for an A_2 system, with the equilibrium concentration of s and a states, is exactly equal to that for an AX system with the same kinds of nuclei. This is true despite the fact that there are 25 per cent of "inert" molecules present.

In general, we shall find that transitions between symmetric and antisymmetric states will be forbidden. A qualitative argument as to why this should be so will be presented a little later, when we consider the difference in magnetic properties between the symmetric (s_0) and antisymmetric (a_0) states of A_2 systems.

Our next problem will be to consider the possibilities for magnetic interaction between two equivalent nuclei. The discussion will be facilitated by setting up a coordinate system in which we shall let the z axis be the direction of the principal magnetic field H (Figure 2-6). A given nucleus centered at zero of the coordinates will have a spin vector $\mathbf{I}$, which will be collinear with its magnetic vector $\boldsymbol{\mu}$. We have already utilized the fact that for any given direction, as along the magnetic field direction z, the magnetic and spin vectors of a nucleus with spin 1/2 will have only two observable average values, which correspond to the quantum numbers $+1/2$ and $-1/2$. The z component of $\boldsymbol{\mu}$ is all we need to compute the energy of a single nucleus in a magnetic field along the z axis. However, when we consider spin-spin interactions between equivalent or nearly equivalent nuclei we have to deal with the vector product $\mathbf{I}(1) \cdot \mathbf{I}(2)$, which, of course, includes the interactions of the x and y compo-

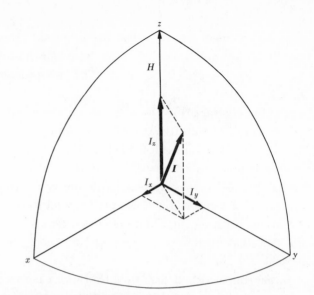

*Figure 2-6   Coordinate system for consideration of inter-
action between a magnetic nucleus and an applied magnetic
field, here taken to be directed along the z axis.*

nents of $\mathbf{I}(1)$ and $\mathbf{I}(2)$ as well as the z components. One
might well ask here why this was not deemed necessary
earlier in treating spin-spin interactions in the AX system
(cf. Section 2-1). We shall not neglect this point; but first it
will be desirable to show how spin-spin interaction energies
can be evaluated.

The spin-spin interaction operator $\mathcal{3C}_{12}$, Equation (2-12),
has the following form for two equivalent or nonequivalent
nuclei:

$$\mathcal{3C}_{12} = J \cdot \mathbf{I}(1) \cdot \mathbf{I}(2) \tag{2-28}$$

$$\mathcal{3C}_{12} = J[I_x(1) \cdot I_x(2) + I_y(1) \cdot I_y(2) + I_z(1) \cdot I_z(2)] \tag{2-29}$$

It can be shown for nuclei of spin $1/2$ that this expression
(2-29) for $\mathcal{3C}_{12}$ is equivalent to the following form:[6]

$$\mathcal{3C}_{12} = (J/4)(2p_{12} - 1) \tag{2-30}$$

The new symbol p_{12} represents a "permutation" operator
that interchanges possible pairs of the specified *index numbers* (here 1 and 2) of the nuclei in product wave functions.

42

Thus,

$$p_{12}|\alpha\beta\rangle = p_{12}|\alpha(1)\beta(2)\rangle = |\alpha(2)\beta(1)\rangle = |\beta(1)\alpha(2)\rangle = |\beta\alpha\rangle$$
$$p_{12}|\alpha\beta\alpha\rangle = p_{12}|\alpha(1)\beta(2)\alpha(3)\rangle = |\alpha(2)\beta(1)\alpha(3)\rangle = |\beta(1)\alpha(2)\alpha(3)\rangle = |\beta\alpha\alpha\rangle$$

$$(2\text{-}31)$$

EXERCISE 2-15

Evaluate (a) $p_{12}|\beta\beta\rangle$, $p_{13}|\alpha\beta\beta\rangle$, (b) $p_{14}|\alpha\alpha\beta\beta\rangle$, and
(c) $p_{13}|\alpha\beta(\alpha\beta - \beta\alpha)\rangle$.

Calculation of the interaction energies corresponding to the wave functions $\alpha\alpha$ and $(1/\sqrt{2})\,(\alpha\beta + \beta\alpha)$ is straight-forward:

$$\langle\alpha\alpha|\,(J/4)(2p_{12} - 1)\,|\alpha\alpha\rangle = (J/4)[2\langle\alpha\alpha|\alpha\alpha\rangle - \langle\alpha\alpha|\alpha\alpha\rangle] = +J/4$$

and

$$\langle(1/\sqrt{2})(\alpha\beta + \beta\alpha)|\,(J/4)(2p_{12} - 1)\,|(1/\sqrt{2})(\alpha\beta + \beta\alpha)\rangle$$
$$= (J/8)[2\langle(\alpha\beta + \beta\alpha)|(\beta\alpha + \alpha\beta)\rangle - \langle(\alpha\beta + \beta\alpha)|(\alpha\beta + \beta\alpha)\rangle] = +J/4$$

$$(2\text{-}32)$$

EXERCISE 2-16

(a) Show that
$$\langle(1/\sqrt{2})(\alpha\beta - \beta\alpha)|\,(J/4)(2p_{12} - 1)\,|(1/\sqrt{2})(\alpha\beta - \beta\alpha)\rangle$$
is equal to $-3J/4$. (b) Evaluate
$$\langle\alpha\alpha\alpha|\,(J/4)[2(p_{12} + p_{13} + p_{23}) - 3]\,|\alpha\alpha\alpha\rangle$$
and
$$\langle\alpha\beta\alpha|\,(J_{12}/4)(2p_{12} - 1) + (J_{13}/4)(2p_{13} - 1)$$
$$+ (J_{23}/4)(2p_{23} - 1)\,|\alpha\beta\alpha\rangle$$

Proceeding similarly for the rest of the possible states, we find the energy levels for the A_2 system with $J = 0$ and $J \neq 0$ given in Table 2-3.

The energy diagram for $J \neq 0$ shows that the energies of the allowed transitions, $s_{-1} \rightarrow s_0$ and $s_0 \rightarrow s_1$, are equal; consequently, these would lead to a single resonance line.

Table 2-3 Energy Levels and Transitions for Two Interacting Equivalent Magnetic Nuclei (A_2, $J > 0$)

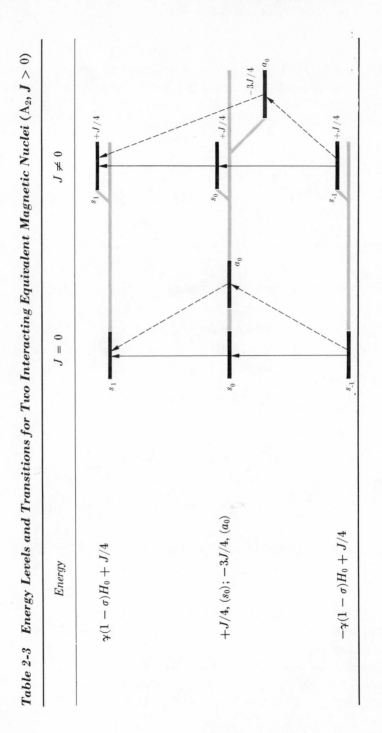

Energy	$J = 0$	$J \neq 0$
$\gamma(1 - \sigma)H_0 + J/4$		
$+J/4$, (s_0); $-3J/4$, (a_0)		
$-\gamma(1 - \sigma)H_0 + J/4$		

The transitions $s_{-1} \rightarrow a_0$ and $a_0 \rightarrow s_1$ differ in energy from the others by $\pm J$. Thus, one would expect to observe a splitting of the resonances of equivalent nuclei by their mutual interaction except for the fact that the $s_{-1} \rightarrow a_0$ and $a_0 \rightarrow s_1$ transitions are strictly forbidden; cf. Equation (2-27).

The fact that the a_0 state is calculated to be more stable than the s_0 state by J energy units is very revealing with respect to the difference between these states, which both have $F_z = 0$. The s_0 state is destabilized by spin-spin interaction (assuming $J > 0$), whereas the a_0 state is strongly stabilized. Indeed, all the s states are equally destabilized, which can be taken to mean that the effective value of the angle between the magnetic moments of the two nuclei is the same in each of the s states. In the a_0 state, the effective value of the angle between the moments must be very different to have such considerable stabilization.

The situation becomes clearer when we consider *nuclear precession*. A magnetic nucleus in a magnetic field H acts as

Figure 2-7 Precession of a nuclear magnetic vector around the axis of an applied magnetic field. The frequency of precession is ν.

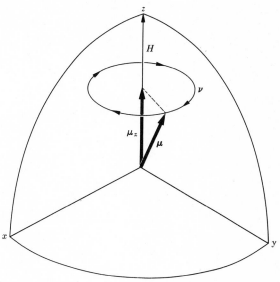

though its magnetic vector $\boldsymbol{\mu}$ precesses around the field axis at the frequency $\nu = \gamma H$, where γ equals γ, the "nuclear gyromagnetic ratio," divided by 2π, and is a constant for each nucleus. The component of $\boldsymbol{\mu}$ along the z axis μ_z remains constant in such precession (see Figure 2-7).

Now, if we have two equivalent nuclei, their magnetic vectors will both have the same ν values, which means that the phase angle θ between them remains constant. Diagrams such as Figure 2-8 are particularly helpful here. For s_{-1} the magnetic vectors $\boldsymbol{\mu}_1$ and $\boldsymbol{\mu}_2$ of nuclei (1) and (2) are both oriented so that their projections on the z axis point in the same direction. The two vectors act as though they precess at a constant phase angle to give a resultant that precesses at the same angular velocity around the field axis. The μ_z of the resultant is the sum of the individual μ_z values of each nucleus.

Figure 2-8   Schematic diagram of the precession of the magnetic vectors of two equivalent nuclei and their resultant for the s_{-1} state around the field axis; $\theta \neq 180°$.

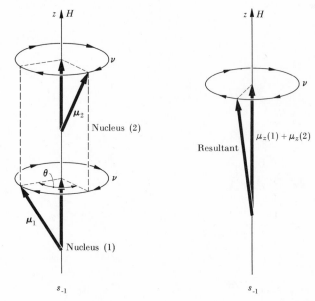

For the s_0 state, I_z of (1) and (2) have opposite signs and F_z and μ_z are both zero. However, μ_x and μ_y cannot both be zero since in all the s states the $\boldsymbol{\mu}_1$ and $\boldsymbol{\mu}_2$ act as if they were at the same effective angle to one another. Figure 2-9 provides a representation of an s_0 state. It is inaccurate in the sense that nuclei (1) and (2) are specifically assigned $I_z = +1/2$ and $-1/2$, respectively. Nonetheless, the diagram is useful to clarify how precessing magnetic vectors of two equivalent nuclei might have no component in the z direction but a large x,y component by maintaining an average phase angle different from 180°. The resultant x,y vector would of course precess around the z axis at the same frequency as its components and would be independent of which nucleus, (1) or (2), had $I_z = \pm 1/2$.

The a_0 state can be expressed by a diagram similar to that for s_0 except that now the effective phase angle is 180°, which

Figure 2-9   Schematic diagram of the precession of the magnetic vectors of two equivalent nuclei and their resultant for the s_0 state; $\theta \neq 180°$.

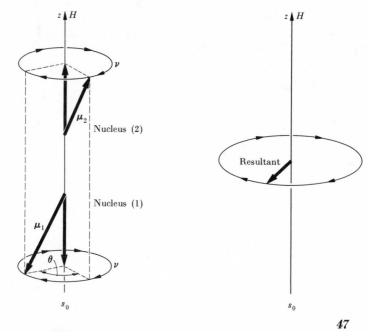

Table 2-4 Energy Levels and Transitions for AX and A₂ Systems of Nuclei with J > 0

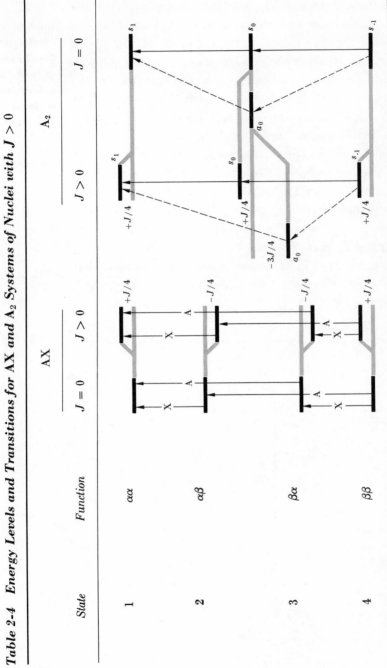

means that this state has no resultant in the x,y plane (Figure 2-10). A state of affairs such as this rationalizes why transitions between the a_0 and the s states are forbidden. The a_0 state has no magnetic moment and thus cannot interact with the field produced by an external rf oscillator. In effect, the oscillator cannot get the necessary "grip" on the nuclei to raise them to a higher energy state.

2-3 *Quantitative treatment of the* AB *system*

The AB system is expected to have a character intermediate between AX and A_2 systems. Let us first consider qualitatively how the energy levels of an AX system change as the chemical-shift difference between A and X diminishes and the system approaches A_2 by way of AB. The extremes, with and without interaction, are shown in Table 2-4. As the chemical shifts of A and X approach one another, states 2 and 3 draw more closely together in energy. We should

Figure 2-10   Schematic diagram of the a_0 state; $\theta = 180°$.

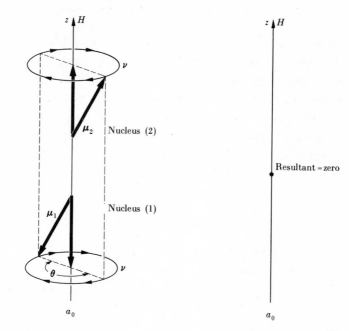

anticipate that the simple symmetric wave functions $\psi_2 = \alpha\beta$ [$= \alpha(A)\beta(X)$], $\psi_3 = \beta\alpha$ [$= \beta(A)\alpha(X)$] must become inadequate descriptions of the two states because, as the nuclei become more nearly equivalent, it becomes less and less permissible to label each nucleus specifically as to quantum number. We can resolve the dilemma by *mixing* the two states 2 and 3 with the intention of obtaining one state corresponding more or less to s_0 and another to a_0. Thus, we might write for a mixed wave function ψ,

$$\psi = a\psi_2 + b\psi_3 \qquad (2\text{-}33)$$

where a and b are "mixing coefficients" that can be positive or negative and which by the normalization condition must be such that $a^2 + b^2 = 1$.

EXERCISE 2-17

(a) Show that, if ψ_2 and ψ_3 are normalized and orthogonal wave functions, $\psi = a\psi_2 + b\psi_3$ is normalized if $a^2 + b^2 = 1$.
(b) Show that the wave functions $\psi = a\psi_2 - b\psi_3$ and $\psi = -a\psi_2 + b\psi_3$ give the same calculated energies.

The values of the coefficients and the energies of the states are most easily calculated by the *variation method*.[7] The idea here is that for the lowest of the two mixed states the coefficients will be such that the energy of the system will be at a minimum value. There will be a corresponding maximum energy state, the coefficients of which are also obtained by the variation method. The wave functions for these two states are orthogonal. We proceed as follows: The energy of the mixed wave function ψ is given by

$$E = \int\psi\mathcal{3C}\psi \, d\phi \Big/ \int\psi^2 \, d\phi = \langle\psi|\mathcal{3C}|\psi\rangle/\langle\psi|\psi\rangle$$

$$= \frac{\langle(a\psi_2 + b\psi_3)|\mathcal{3C}|(a\psi_2 + b\psi_3)\rangle}{\langle(a\psi_2 + b\psi_3)|(a\psi_2 + b\psi_3)\rangle} \qquad (2\text{-}34)$$

$$E = \frac{a^2\langle\psi_2|\mathcal{3C}|\psi_2\rangle + b^2\langle\psi_3|\mathcal{3C}|\psi_3\rangle + ab\langle\psi_2|\mathcal{3C}|\psi_3\rangle + ab\langle\psi_3|\mathcal{3C}|\psi_2\rangle}{a^2 + b^2} \qquad (2\text{-}35)$$

where $\langle \psi_2 | \psi_2 \rangle$ and $\langle \psi_3 | \psi_3 \rangle$ have been taken as unity and $\langle \psi_2 | \psi_3 \rangle$ as zero. Noting that $\langle \psi_2 | \mathfrak{IC} | \psi_3 \rangle = \langle \psi_3 | \mathfrak{IC} | \psi_2 \rangle$, then

$$E = \frac{a^2 \langle \psi_2 | \mathfrak{IC} | \psi_2 \rangle + b^2 \langle \psi_3 | \mathfrak{IC} | \psi_3 \rangle + 2ab \langle \psi_2 | \mathfrak{IC} | \psi_3 \rangle}{a^2 + b^2} \tag{2-36}$$

where all the integrals are of types already evaluated in this chapter; e.g., $\langle \alpha\beta | \mathfrak{IC} | \alpha\beta \rangle$, $\langle \alpha\beta | \mathfrak{IC} | \beta\alpha \rangle$, etc.

EXERCISE 2-18

Show that $\langle \psi_2 | \mathfrak{IC} | \psi_3 \rangle$ has the same value as $\langle \psi_3 | \mathfrak{IC} | \psi_2 \rangle$ for $\psi_2 = \alpha\beta$ and $\psi_3 = \beta\alpha$.

EXERCISE 2-19

Use Equation (2-36) and plot E as a function of a/b (both positive and negative values) with $\langle \psi_2 | \mathfrak{IC} | \psi_2 \rangle$ taken as $+1$ cps and $\langle \psi_3 | \mathfrak{IC} | \psi_3 \rangle$ as -9 cps. Take $J = 16$ cps and remember that $a^2 + b^2 = 1$. Determine approximately the maximum and minimum values of E and the values of a and b that correspond thereto.

To find the minimum and maximum values of E we take partial differentials with respect to a and b and set $\partial E / \partial a$ and $\partial E / \partial b$ equal to zero. This is conveniently done by re-arrangement of Equation (2-36) before differentiation:

$$a^2 E + b^2 E = a^2 \langle \psi_2 | \mathfrak{IC} | \psi_2 \rangle + b^2 \langle \psi_3 | \mathfrak{IC} | \psi_3 \rangle + 2ab \langle \psi_2 | \mathfrak{IC} | \psi_3 \rangle \tag{2-37}$$

Differentiating with respect to a and setting $\partial E / \partial a$ equal to zero gives

$$2aE + a^2 (\partial E / \partial a) + b^2 (\partial E / \partial a) = 2a \langle \psi_2 | \mathfrak{IC} | \psi_2 \rangle + 2b \langle \psi_2 | \mathfrak{IC} | \psi_3 \rangle$$
$$aE = a \langle \psi_2 | \mathfrak{IC} | \psi_2 \rangle + b \langle \psi_2 | \mathfrak{IC} | \psi_3 \rangle$$

or

$$a(\langle \psi_2 | \mathfrak{IC} | \psi_2 \rangle - E) + b \langle \psi_2 | \mathfrak{IC} | \psi_3 \rangle = 0 \tag{2-38}$$

Similarly, differentiating with respect to b gives

$$a^2 (\partial E / \partial b) + 2bE + b^2 (\partial E / \partial b) = 2b \langle \psi_3 | \mathfrak{IC} | \psi_3 \rangle + 2a \langle \psi_2 | \mathfrak{IC} | \psi_3 \rangle$$

and

$$a \langle \psi_2 | \mathfrak{IC} | \psi_3 \rangle + b(\langle \psi_3 | \mathfrak{IC} | \psi_3 \rangle - E) = 0 \tag{2-39}$$

The simultaneous "secular" equations (2-38) and (2-39) have $a = b = 0$ as a trivial solution, which violates the condition we impose—that $a^2 + b^2 = 1$. Nontrivial solutions can be obtained for those values of E that satisfy the "secular" determinant:

$$\begin{vmatrix} \langle \psi_2 | \mathfrak{K} | \psi_2 \rangle - E & \langle \psi_2 | \mathfrak{K} | \psi_3 \rangle \\ \langle \psi_2 | \mathfrak{K} | \psi_3 \rangle & \langle \psi_3 | \mathfrak{K} | \psi_3 \rangle - E \end{vmatrix} = 0 \qquad (2\text{-}40)$$

which breaks down to

$$(\langle \psi_2 | \mathfrak{K} | \psi_2 \rangle - E)(\langle \psi_3 | \mathfrak{K} | \psi_3 \rangle - E) - (\langle \psi_2 | \mathfrak{K} | \psi_3 \rangle)^2 = 0$$

and

$$E^2 - (\langle \psi_2 | \mathfrak{K} | \psi_2 \rangle + \langle \psi_3 | \mathfrak{K} | \psi_3 \rangle)E + (\langle \psi_2 | \mathfrak{K} | \psi_2 \rangle)(\langle \psi_3 | \mathfrak{K} | \psi_3 \rangle)$$
$$- (\langle \psi_2 | \mathfrak{K} | \psi_3 \rangle)^2 = 0 \qquad (2\text{-}41)$$

For each of the two values of E, which are the roots of the quadratic equation (2-41), we can compute corresponding values of a and b, which of course for our final wave functions must meet the condition $a^2 + b^2 = 1$.

EXERCISE 2-20

Verify that Equation (2-41) can be obtained from Equation (2-40).

Fortunately, in the general case of mixed nuclear wave functions, we can write down the secular equations and determinant very quickly, although the solutions thereof may be tedious or practically impossible without the use of a high-speed digital computer. Thus, for $\psi = c_1\psi_1 + c_2\psi_2 + \cdots + c_n\psi_n$, where the ψ_n are mutually orthogonal and normalized,

$$c_1(\langle \psi_1 | \mathfrak{K} | \psi_1 \rangle - E) + c_2\langle \psi_1 | \mathfrak{K} | \psi_2 \rangle + \cdots + c_n\langle \psi_1 | \mathfrak{K} | \psi_n \rangle = 0$$
$$c_1\langle \psi_2 | \mathfrak{K} | \psi_1 \rangle + c_2(\langle \psi_2 | \mathfrak{K} | \psi_2 \rangle - E) + \cdots + c_n\langle \psi_2 | \mathfrak{K} | \psi_n \rangle = 0$$
$$\vdots$$
$$\vdots$$
$$c_1\langle \psi_n | \mathfrak{K} | \psi_1 \rangle + c_2\langle \psi_n | \mathfrak{K} | \psi_2 \rangle + \cdots + c_n(\langle \psi_n | \mathfrak{K} | \psi_n \rangle - E) = 0$$

$$(2\text{-}42)$$

and

$$
\begin{vmatrix}
\langle\psi_1|\mathfrak{IC}|\psi_1\rangle - E & \langle\psi_1|\mathfrak{IC}|\psi_2\rangle & \cdots & \langle\psi_1|\mathfrak{IC}|\psi_n\rangle \\
\langle\psi_2|\mathfrak{IC}|\psi_1\rangle & \langle\psi_2|\mathfrak{IC}|\psi_2\rangle - E & \cdots & \langle\psi_2|\mathfrak{IC}|\psi_n\rangle \\
\vdots & \vdots & & \vdots \\
\langle\psi_n|\mathfrak{IC}|\psi_1\rangle & \langle\psi_n|\mathfrak{IC}|\psi_2\rangle & \cdots & \langle\psi_n|\mathfrak{IC}|\psi_n\rangle - E
\end{vmatrix} = 0 \qquad (2\text{-}43)
$$

If we remember that $\langle\psi_n|\mathfrak{IC}|\psi_m\rangle = \langle\psi_m|\mathfrak{IC}|\psi_n\rangle$, we can rewrite the determinant [Equation (2-43)] as shown in Equation (2-44).

$$
\begin{vmatrix}
\langle\psi_1|\mathfrak{IC}|\psi_1\rangle - E & \langle\psi_1|\mathfrak{IC}|\psi_2\rangle & \cdots & \langle\psi_1|\mathfrak{IC}|\psi_n\rangle \\
\langle\psi_1|\mathfrak{IC}|\psi_2\rangle & \langle\psi_2|\mathfrak{IC}|\psi_2\rangle - E & \cdots & \langle\psi_2|\mathfrak{IC}|\psi_n\rangle \\
\vdots & \vdots & & \vdots \\
\langle\psi_1|\mathfrak{IC}|\psi_n\rangle & \langle\psi_2|\mathfrak{IC}|\psi_n\rangle & \cdots & \langle\psi_n|\mathfrak{IC}|\psi_n\rangle - E
\end{vmatrix} = 0 \qquad (2\text{-}44)
$$

EXERCISE 2-21

Set up the secular determinant for the wave function $\psi = c_1\alpha\alpha + c_2\alpha\beta + c_3\beta\alpha + c_4\beta\beta$ and evaluate each element for an AB case with $\sigma_A \neq \sigma_B$ and $J_{AB} \neq 0$. What conclusions can you reach about mixing of states with different values of F_z?

EXERCISE 2-22

Show that the variation method applied to the function $\psi = c_1\alpha\beta + c_2\beta\alpha$ when nuclei (1) and (2) are equivalent leads to the energies and wave functions previously obtained for the states of the A_2 case with $F_z = 0$.

To complete our discussion of AB systems we need to work out the energy levels from Equation (2-41) more explicitly, and thence the energies of the various transitions. Finally, we shall compute the coefficients of the mixed wave functions and the relative transition probabilities. First, we

Table 2-5 Comparison of Energy Levels and Transitions for AX and AB Systems

F_z	$J = 0$ Energy	State	$J > 0$ Energy
$+1$	$(\gamma H_0/2)(2 - \sigma_A - \sigma_B)$	1	$+J/4 + (\gamma H_0/2)(2 - \sigma_A - \sigma_B)$
0	$(\gamma H_0/2)(\sigma_B - \sigma_A)$	2	$-J/4 + (1/2)\sqrt{J^2 + \gamma^2 H_0^2(\sigma_A - \sigma_B)^2}$
0	$(\gamma H_0/2)(\sigma_A - \sigma_B)$	3	$-J/4 - (1/2)\sqrt{J^2 + \gamma^2 H_0^2(\sigma_A - \sigma_B)^2}$
-1	$-(\gamma H_0/2)(2 - \sigma_A - \sigma_B)$	4	$+J/4 - (\gamma H_0/2)(2 - \sigma_A - \sigma_B)$

Transition labels: "A_2", "B_2", "A_1", "B_1", A, B

evaluate the integrals of Equation (2-41) letting A be nucleus (1) and B be nucleus (2):

$$\langle \psi_2 | \mathcal{H} | \psi_2 \rangle = \langle \alpha\beta | \mathcal{H}_1 + \mathcal{H}_2 + \mathcal{H}_{12} | \alpha\beta \rangle$$

$$= \langle \alpha | \mathcal{H}_1 | \alpha \rangle + \langle \beta | \mathcal{H}_2 | \beta \rangle + \langle \alpha\beta | (J/4)(2p_{12} - 1) | \alpha\beta \rangle$$

$$= (\gamma H_0/2)(\sigma_B - \sigma_A) - J/4 \tag{2-45}$$

$$\langle \psi_3 | \mathcal{H} | \psi_3 \rangle = \langle \beta\alpha | \mathcal{H}_1 + \mathcal{H}_2 + \mathcal{H}_{12} | \beta\alpha \rangle$$

$$= (\gamma H_0/2)(\sigma_A - \sigma_B) - J/4 \tag{2-46}$$

$$\langle \psi_2 | \mathcal{H} | \psi_3 \rangle = \langle \alpha\beta | \mathcal{H}_1 + \mathcal{H}_2 + \mathcal{H}_{12} | \beta\alpha \rangle$$

$$= J/2 \tag{2-47}$$

If we substitute in Equation (2-41) and then solve for E we get

$$E = -J/4 \pm (1/2)\sqrt{J^2 + \gamma^2 H_0^2 (\sigma_A - \sigma_B)^2} \tag{2-48}$$

We can quickly verify this equation in the limits. When A and B are equivalent, $\sigma_A - \sigma_B = 0$ and the energies of the two mixed states are $+J/4$ and $-3J/4$, as correspond, respectively, to the s_0 and a_0 states of the A_2 system. When $\gamma H_0(\sigma_A - \sigma_B)$ (the chemical shift) $\gg J$ (the coupling), then the values of E are $-J/4 \pm (\gamma H_0/2)$ $(\sigma_A - \sigma_B)$, which are the energies previously obtained for states 2 and 3 of an AX system.

EXERCISE 2-23

Show that the matrix elements found in Equations (2-45) to (2-47) are the same as those derived by use of Equations (6-31) to (6-33) of Ref. 1.

The energy levels for the AB system with and without spin-spin interaction are shown in Table 2-5.

When $J = 0$ the transitions between the states can be clearly designated as A or B transitions, the distinction being based on which nucleus changes its I_z number. The situation is more complex when $J \neq 0$, because no clean-cut distinction is possible then as to whether A or B has $I_z = +1/2$ for the mixed states. We can call certain transitions "A" or A-type transitions by virtue of the fact that, as J becomes smaller with respect to the chemical shift, these transitions approach the true A transitions at the limit.

EXERCISE 2-24

Calculate the energies of all the states for the AB case described in Exercise 2-19 and compare the answers with those obtained graphically. Calculate the energy changes for all the transitions in which $\Delta F_z = +1$ and sketch out the expected resonance spectrum for this system, showing the positions of the lines on a cycles-per-second scale. Label each line with the transition to which it corresponds, i.e., "A," "B," etc. Calculate the line positions that would be expected at a four-times-greater magnetic field.

It will be seen from Exercise 2-24 that none of the transition energies of the AB system correspond to the chemical-shift difference between A and B. Therefore, in the analysis of an AB pattern, although J can be obtained directly, the chemical shift has to be computed from J and the separation between the "A" and "B" resonances.

Figure 2-11   Typical **AB** *nuclear resonance spectrum at 60 Mc.*

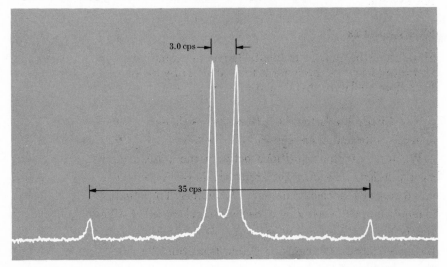

EXERCISE 2-25

Determine J and the chemical shift in cycles per second for the 60-Mc AB spectrum shown in Figure 2-11.

EXERCISE 2-26

Show that the spacing between the centers of the "A" and "B" doublets in an AB spectrum is equal to

$$\sqrt{J^2 + \gamma^2 H_0{}^2(\sigma_A - \sigma_B)^2}$$

Quantum
Mechanical
Treatment
of Spin-Spin
Interaction
between
Two Nuclei

Calculation of the mixing coefficients a and b for the equation $\psi = a\psi_2 + b\psi_3$ is most conveniently done by the following procedure, which has general utility. The ratios of coefficients corresponding to solutions of sets of secular equations like Equation (2-42) are equal to the ratios of the *cofactors* of the derived secular determinants. Thus, for the general case,

$$\frac{c_1}{c_2} = \frac{\text{cofactor}_1}{\text{cofactor}_2}$$

$$+ \begin{vmatrix} \langle \psi_2 | \mathcal{H} | \psi_2 \rangle - E & \cdots & \langle \psi_2 | \mathcal{H} | \psi_n \rangle \\ \vdots & \ddots & \vdots \\ \langle \psi_2 | \mathcal{H} | \psi_n \rangle & \cdots & \langle \psi_n | \mathcal{H} | \psi_n \rangle - E \end{vmatrix}$$

$$- \begin{vmatrix} \langle \psi_1 | \mathcal{H} | \psi_2 \rangle & \langle \psi_2 | \mathcal{H} | \psi_3 \rangle & \cdots & \langle \psi_2 | \mathcal{H} | \psi_n \rangle \\ \vdots & \vdots & \ddots & \vdots \\ \langle \psi_1 | \mathcal{H} | \psi_n \rangle & \langle \psi_3 | \mathcal{H} | \psi_n \rangle & \cdots & \langle \psi_n | \mathcal{H} | \psi_n \rangle - E \end{vmatrix}$$

$$(2-49)$$

The cofactor of c_i is seen to be the secular determinant, Equation (2-44), with both the top row and ith vertical column removed. Thus, if $i = 1$, the top row and far-left-hand column are removed to get cofactor$_1$. The cofactors can be taken as positive when i is an odd integer and negative when i is an even integer. The cofactors are dependent, of course, on the E values that satisfy the secular equations, and the ratios of coefficients must be normalized for the final wave function.

It can readily be seen that computation of ratios of the coefficients for each permitted value of E is by no means a trivial task when the number of coefficients is large. Fortunately, computations of this type can be made by standard programs for high-speed digital computers.

For the AB system, we have used a for c_2 and b for c_3. The determinant, Equation (2-40), then affords

$$a/b = \text{cofactor}_2/\text{cofactor}_3 = -(\langle\psi_3|\mathcal{H}|\psi_3\rangle - E)/\langle\psi_2|\mathcal{H}|\psi_3\rangle \tag{2-50}$$

Taking the values of the integrals from Equations (2-45) to (2-47), we then have

$$a/b = -[\gamma H_0(\sigma_A - \sigma_B)/2 - (J/4) - E]/(J/2)$$

and substituting for E in Equation (2-48),

$$a/b = [-\gamma H_0(\sigma_A - \sigma_B) \pm \sqrt{J^2 + \gamma^2 H_0{}^2(\sigma_A - \sigma_B)^2}]/J \tag{2-51}$$

The final coefficients must of course meet the normalization condition; i.e., $a^2 + b^2 = 1$.

EXERCISE 2-27

Calculate the coefficients for the normalized mixed wave functions for the AB system described in Exercises 2-19 and 2-24 at the specified magnetic field and one that is four times as intense. Compare the calculated a/b with the graphical value obtained previously.

To calculate the transition probabilities P_{ij} for the changes in nuclear energy states shown in Table 2-5, we can use the procedure illustrated by Equation (2-18). For $P_{4,2}$, the probability corresponding to the change in wave function $\beta\beta \rightarrow (a\alpha\beta + b\beta\alpha)$, which is an "A" transition,

$$
\begin{aligned}
P_{4,2} &= [\langle(a\alpha\beta + b\beta\alpha)|F_+|\beta\beta\rangle]^2 \\
&= [a(\langle\alpha\beta|\alpha\beta\rangle + \langle\alpha\beta|\beta\alpha\rangle) + b(\langle\beta\alpha|\alpha\beta\rangle + \langle\beta\alpha|\beta\alpha\rangle)]^2 \\
&= [a + b]^2 \\
&= a^2 + 2ab + b^2
\end{aligned} \tag{2-52}
$$

or, since $a^2 + b^2 = 1$,

$$P_{4,2} = 1 + 2ab \qquad (2\text{-}53)$$

For the a and b values of Equations (2-52) and (2-53), the wave function for state 3 is $(b\alpha\beta - a\beta\alpha)$ so the other "A" transition is $(b\alpha\beta - a\beta\alpha) \rightarrow \alpha\alpha$, and for this

$$P_{3,1} = [b - a]^2 = 1 - 2ab \qquad (2\text{-}54)$$

Therefore, the ratio of the intensities of the "A" resonances are predicted to be

$$P_{3,1}/P_{4,2} = (1 - 2ab)/(1 + 2ab) = [a - b]^2/[a + b]^2$$
$$= [1 - a/b]^2/[1 + a/b]^2 \qquad (2\text{-}55)$$

EXERCISE 2-28

(*a*) Derive an expression like Equation (2-55) for the ratio of the "B" transition probabilities $P_{2,1}/P_{4,3}$; calculate $P_{3,1}/P_{4,2}$ and $P_{2,1}/P_{4,3}$ for the system described in Exercises 2-19, 2-24, and 2-27. (*b*) Calculate the transition probabilities expected for the AB spectrum in Figure 2-11. Calculate what this spectrum should look like at 30 Mc.

Figure 2-12   Nuclear resonance spectrum showing a symmetrical quartet of resonance lines.

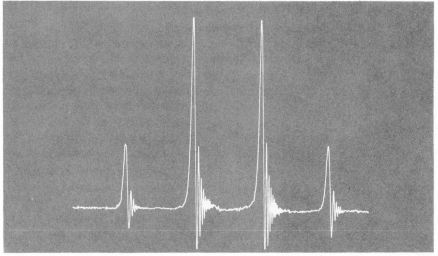

The last form of Equation (2-55) is particularly useful because we have already derived an expression for a/b [Equation (2-51)] in terms of J and the chemical shift.

EXERCISE 2-29

Determine whether or not the spectrum of Figure 2-12 is that of an AB system.

References
1. J. A. Pople, W. G. Schneider, and H. J. Bernstein, "High-resolution Nuclear Magnetic Resonance," McGraw-Hill Book Company, Inc., New York, 1959, p. 98.
2. J. D. Roberts, "Nuclear Magnetic Resonance. Applications to Organic Chemistry," McGraw-Hill Book Company, Inc., New York, 1959, pp. 84–85.
3. C. A. Coulson, "Valence," Oxford University Press, London, 1952, pp. 49–50.
4. Ref. 3, pp. 15–16; J. D. Roberts, "Notes on Molecular Orbital Calculations," W. A. Benjamin, Inc., New York, 1961, Chap. 2.
5. Ref. 3, pp. 54–56.
6. P. A. M. Dirac, "The Principles of Quantum Mechanics," 3rd ed., Oxford University Press, London, 1947, p. 222.
7. Ref. 3, Chap. III, pp. 54–64.

FOR the treatment of multiple-spin systems it will be desirable to rephrase some of our basic equations to give them greater generality. The Hamiltonian operator thus becomes

$$\mathfrak{IC} = \mathfrak{IC}^{(0)} + \mathfrak{IC}^{(1)} \tag{3-1}$$

where $\mathfrak{IC}^{(0)}$ gives the sum of the interactions of the nuclei with the stationary applied field H_0 and $\mathfrak{IC}^{(1)}$ gives the sum of the spin-spin interactions of the pairs of nuclei. Thus, for i nuclei,

$$\mathfrak{IC}^{(0)} = \sum_i \gamma_i(1 - \sigma_i)H_0 I_z(i) \tag{3-2}$$

$$\mathfrak{IC}^{(0)} = \sum_i \nu_i I_z(i) \tag{3-3}$$

where $\nu_i = \gamma_i(1 - \sigma_i)H_0$ and is in cycles per second if γ_i is in cycles per second per gauss.* And

$$\mathfrak{IC}^{(1)} = \sum_{i<j} J_{ij}\mathbf{I}(i)\cdot\mathbf{I}(j) \tag{3-4}$$

$$\mathfrak{IC}^{(1)} = (1/4) \sum_{i<j} J_{ij}(2p_{ij} - 1) \tag{3-5}$$

These changes are desirable because, with three nuclei, we have to consider J_{12}, J_{13}, and J_{23} and, with four nuclei, J_{12}, J_{13}, J_{14}, J_{23}, J_{24}, and J_{34}. In many cases, some of these couplings are equal or of such a nature as not to affect the appearance of the resonance spectrum.

For three nuclei there are several cases of interest, which can be symbolized as A_3, AB_2, ABC, AX_2, ABX, and AMX —the last being three independent nuclei with all chemical

* In the ensuing discussion we shall also often use ν to denote freqencies relative to a standard since this is the normal procedure in analyzing spectra.

shifts much larger than the respective coupling constants. The analysis of these systems varies from simple for AMX to difficult for ABC. First, we shall work out the energy levels for AMX, since the other three nucleus systems tend to approach this one when the chemical shifts are large with respect to the couplings.

EXERCISE 3-1

Write structures of organic molecules that would have protons so disposed as to constitute examples of A_3, AB_2, ABC, AX_2, ABX, and AMX systems.

EXERCISE 3-2

Analysis of the A_3 system by the procedure used in Exercise 2-22 for the A_2 system involves the solution of two third-order determinants in the variation treatment of $\psi = c_1\beta\beta\alpha + c_2\beta\alpha\beta + c_3\alpha\beta\beta$ when $F_z = -1/2$ and $\psi = c_1\alpha\alpha\beta + c_2\alpha\beta\alpha + c_3\beta\alpha\alpha$ when $F_z = +1/2$. A satisfactory set of final wave functions turns out to be $(\beta\beta\alpha + \beta\alpha\beta + \alpha\beta\beta)/\sqrt{3}$, $(\beta\beta\alpha + \beta\alpha\beta - 2\alpha\beta\beta)/\sqrt{6}$, and $(\beta\beta\alpha - \beta\alpha\beta)/\sqrt{2}$ for $F_z = -1/2$; and $(\alpha\alpha\beta + \alpha\beta\alpha + \beta\alpha\alpha)/\sqrt{3}$, $(\alpha\alpha\beta + \alpha\beta\alpha - 2\beta\alpha\alpha)/\sqrt{6}$, and $(\alpha\alpha\beta - \alpha\beta\alpha)/\sqrt{2}$ for $F_z = +1/2$. The couplings between the various pairs in an A_3 system are by definition equal, and therefore a single J suffices. Use the above

Table 3-1   Wave Functions and Energies for States of AMX Systems

State	F_z*	Function	Energy
1	$+3/2$	$\alpha\alpha\alpha$	$(\nu_A + \nu_M + \nu_X)/2 + (J_{AM} + J_{AX} + J_{MX})/4$
2	$+1/2$	$\alpha\alpha\beta$	$(\nu_A + \nu_M - \nu_X)/2 + (J_{AM} - J_{AX} - J_{MX})/4$
3	$+1/2$	$\alpha\beta\alpha$	$(\nu_A - \nu_M + \nu_X)/2 + (-J_{AM} + J_{AX} - J_{MX})/4$
4	$+1/2$	$\beta\alpha\alpha$	$(-\nu_A + \nu_M + \nu_X)/2 + (-J_{AM} - J_{AX} + J_{MX})/4$
5	$-1/2$	$\alpha\beta\beta$	$-(-\nu_A + \nu_M + \nu_X)/2 + (-J_{AM} - J_{AX} + J_{MX})/4$
6	$-1/2$	$\beta\alpha\beta$	$-(\nu_A - \nu_M + \nu_X)/2 + (-J_{AM} + J_{AX} - J_{MX})/4$
7	$-1/2$	$\beta\beta\alpha$	$-(\nu_A + \nu_M - \nu_X)/2 + (J_{AM} - J_{AX} - J_{MX})/4$
8	$-3/2$	$\beta\beta\beta$	$-(\nu_A + \nu_M + \nu_X)/2 + (J_{AM} + J_{AX} + J_{MX})/4$

* $F_z = \Sigma_i I_z(i)$.

wave functions and $\alpha\alpha\alpha$ and $\beta\beta\beta$ to construct the energy levels of an A_3 system taking $\nu_A = 0$ and $J = 10$ cps. Calculate the transition energies and probabilities for those transitions having $\Delta F_z = +1$.

3-1 The AMX and AX₂ systems

For the AMX system, we have spin functions, F_z values, and energies as shown in Table 3-1. We shall work out the energy of $\beta\beta\beta$ as an illustrative example on the assumption that $\gamma_A = \gamma_M = \gamma_X = \gamma$ (see also Exercise 2-16).

$$E_8 = \langle \beta\beta\beta \mid \sum_i \nu_i I_z(i) + (1/4) \sum_{i<j} J_{ij}(2p_{ij} - 1) \mid \beta\beta\beta \rangle$$

$$= -\langle \beta \mid \beta \rangle (\nu_A + \nu_M + \nu_X)/2 + [J_{AM} + J_{AX} + J_{MX}]\langle \beta\beta\beta \mid \beta\beta\beta \rangle/4 \quad (3\text{-}6)$$

$$E_8 = -(\nu_A + \nu_M + \nu_X)/2 + (J_{AM} + J_{AX} + J_{MX})/4 \quad (3\text{-}7)$$

The transitions for which $\Delta F_z = +1$ are listed in Table 3-2. There are twelve possible A, M, and X transitions, all of which are equally allowed. The combination transitions 13,

Table 3-2   Transition Energies for AMX Systems

No.	Transition	Origin	Energy
1	$4 \rightarrow 1$	A	$\nu_A + J_{AM}/2 + J_{AX}/2$
2	$6 \rightarrow 2$	A	$\nu_A + J_{AM}/2 - J_{AX}/2$
3	$7 \rightarrow 3$	A	$\nu_A - J_{AM}/2 + J_{AX}/2$
4	$8 \rightarrow 5$	A	$\nu_A - J_{AM}/2 - J_{AX}/2$
5	$2 \rightarrow 1$	X	$\nu_X + J_{AX}/2 + J_{MX}/2$
6	$5 \rightarrow 3$	X	$\nu_X + J_{AX}/2 - J_{MX}/2$
7	$6 \rightarrow 4$	X	$\nu_X - J_{AX}/2 + J_{MX}/2$
8	$8 \rightarrow 7$	X	$\nu_X - J_{AX}/2 - J_{MX}/2$
9	$3 \rightarrow 1$	M	$\nu_M + J_{AM}/2 + J_{MX}/2$
10	$5 \rightarrow 2$	M	$\nu_M + J_{AM}/2 - J_{MX}/2$
11	$7 \rightarrow 4$	M	$\nu_M - J_{AM}/2 + J_{MX}/2$
12	$8 \rightarrow 6$	M	$\nu_M - J_{AM}/2 - J_{MX}/2$
13	$5 \rightarrow 4$	Comb.	$-\nu_A + \nu_M + \nu_X$
14	$7 \rightarrow 2$	Comb.	$\nu_A + \nu_M - \nu_X$
15	$6 \rightarrow 3$	Comb.	$\nu_A - \nu_M + \nu_X$

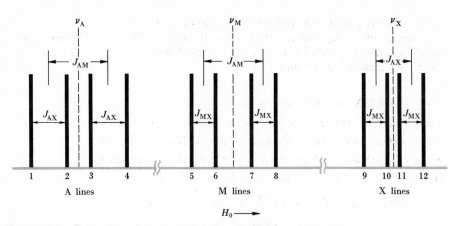

Figure 3-1 ***Resonance-line positions for an AMX system with***
$\nu_A > \nu_M > \nu_X$ ***and*** $J_{AM} > J_{AX} > J_{MX}$. ***The numbers along the***
abscissa correspond to the transition numbers of Table 3-2.
H_0 ***is here considered to be expressed in frequency units.***

14, and 15 are easily shown to be forbidden. On this basis,
if $\nu_A > \nu_M > \nu_X$ and $J_{AM} > J_{AX} > J_{MX}$, the expected
spectrum is as shown in Figure 3-1, in which the dotted
lines represent the positions of ν_A, ν_M, and ν_X.

EXERCISE 3-3

Set up the wave functions and expressions for the energies of the states, the transition energies, and the
transition probabilities for the general case of an AX_2
system. The problem is considerably simplified by the
use of $\alpha(\alpha\beta + \beta\alpha)/\sqrt{2}$ and $\alpha(\alpha\beta - \beta\alpha)/\sqrt{2}$ in place
of $\alpha\beta\alpha$ and $\alpha\alpha\beta$ when $F_z = +1/2$, and $\beta(\alpha\beta + \beta\alpha)/\sqrt{2}$
and $\beta(\alpha\beta - \beta\alpha)/\sqrt{2}$ when $F_z = -1/2$. These sub-
stitutions follow from the equivalence of the X nuclei.
Note that because the chemical shift between A and X
is large compared to J_{AX}, none of the states with different values of I_z for A mix with the other states having the same F_z.

The calculated AMX spectrum is the same as that expected on the simple zero-order basis. [1] If M and X are
equivalent (AX_2 system) so that $\nu_X = \nu_M$, $J_{AX} = J_{AM}$,
then we should expect the A part of the spectrum to simplify

to a 1:2:1 triplet because transitions 2 and 3 would coincide. The X (or M) part of the spectrum might be expected to be more complex because two couplings are involved: J_{AX} and J_{XX}. As is seen from Exercise 3-3, however, all the transitions resulting in observation of splittings corresponding to J_{XX} are forbidden, and the allowed transitions give rise to a symmetrical doublet for X having the separation J_{AX} (see Figure 3-2).

3-2   The AB$_2$ system

The AB$_2$ system is particularly interesting by comparison with AX$_2$ because of the number of lines that it gives. One might expect from a comparison of AX with AB that, in a gradual transition between AX$_2$ and A$_3$ by way of AB$_2$, the positions of the lines and their relative intensities would change, but one would hardly anticipate that new lines would appear. Nonetheless, detailed analysis reveals that a maximum of *nine* lines should be observed. The basis of this analysis will now be discussed.

Figure 3-2   Schematic spectrum for an AX$_2$ system. The numbering of the transitions corresponds to that of Table 3-4.

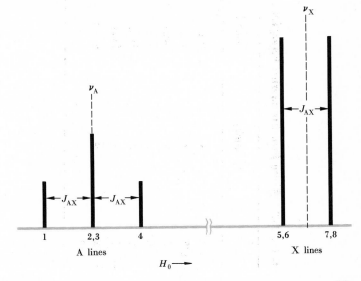

Table 3-3 Wave Functions and Energies for States of AX$_2$ Systems

F_z	Symmetry	Symbol	Wave function	Energy
$+3/2$	s	$s_{3/2}$	$\alpha\alpha\alpha$	$\nu_X + \nu_A/2 + J_{AX}/2 + J_{XX}/4$
$+1/2$	s	$1s_{1/2}$	$\alpha(\alpha\beta + \beta\alpha)/\sqrt{2}$	$\nu_A/2 + J_{XX}/4$
$+1/2$	s	$2s_{1/2}$	$\beta\alpha\alpha$	$\nu_X - \nu_A/2 - J_{AX}/2 + J_{XX}/4$
$+1/2$	a	$a_{1/2}$	$\alpha(\alpha\beta - \beta\alpha)/\sqrt{2}$	$\nu_A/2 - 3J_{XX}/4$
$-1/2$	s	$1s_{-1/2}$	$\alpha\beta\beta$	$-\nu_X + \nu_A/2 - J_{AX}/2 + J_{XX}/4$
$-1/2$	s	$2s_{-1/2}$	$\beta(\alpha\beta + \beta\alpha)/\sqrt{2}$	$-\nu_A/2 + J_{XX}/4$
$-1/2$	a	$a_{-1/2}$	$\beta(\alpha\beta - \beta\alpha)/\sqrt{2}$	$-\nu_A/2 - 3J_{XX}/4$
$-3/2$	s	$s_{-3/2}$	$\beta\beta\beta$	$-\nu_X - \nu_A/2 + J_{AX}/2 + J_{XX}/4$

Our starting point (see Table 3-3) will be the AX_2 wave functions derived in Exercise 3-3. As mentioned before, the value of J_{XX} does not influence the observed spectrum in any way because all the s states are increased in energy by $J_{XX}/4$, the a states are decreased by $-3J_{XX}/4$, and no transitions are allowed between the a and s states. Therefore, we shall set $J_{XX} = 0$ in the analysis that is to follow.

In the AB_2 system, $\nu_A - \nu_B$ is comparable to J_{AB}; this means that there is mixing of the $1s_{1/2}$ and $2s_{1/2}$ and of $1s_{-1/2}$ and $2s_{-1/2}$ states. The mathematical treatment of AB_2 thus consists in part of solving the resulting pair of two-row determinants. The mixing of the states can qualitatively be seen to result in modification of the AX_2 energy levels, as shown in Table 3-4.

The AX_2 system in the absence of spin-spin interaction gives four equal A transitions of energy ν_A and four equal X transitions of energy ν_X. When J_{AX} is greater than zero, two of the X transitions (5 and 6) have the energy $\nu_X + J_{AX}/2$ while the other two (7 and 8) have the energy $\nu_X - J_{AX}/2$. The A transitions have the respective energies $\nu_A + J_{AX}$ (1), ν_A (2 and 3), and $\nu_A - J_{AX}$ (4). For both these situations ($J_{AX} = 0$ and $J_{AX} \neq 0$), the combination transition $1s_{-1/2} \rightarrow 2s_{1/2}$ can easily be shown to have zero probability.

In the AB_2 system, mixing of $1s_{1/2}$ and $2s_{1/2}$ states leads to two new states, the higher of which we shall label $1s'_{1/2}$ and the lower $2s'_{1/2}$. In the same way, mixing of $1s_{-1/2}$ and $2s_{-1/2}$ leads to $1s'_{-1/2}$ and $2s'_{-1/2}$. The mixing of these pairs of states does not occur equally because $1s_{-1/2}$ and $2s_{-1/2}$ are closer together in energy than are $1s_{1/2}$ and $2s_{1/2}$. The result is to greatly increase the complexity of the spectrum because none of the four B′ transitions are now equal to one another (or to ν_B or $\nu_B \pm J_{AB}$). Similarly, none of the three A′ transitions are equal to one another. However, the $(a_{-1/2} \rightarrow a_{1/2})$ A transition is unchanged by mixing and

Table 3-4 Comparison of Energy Levels of AX_2 and AB_2 Systems

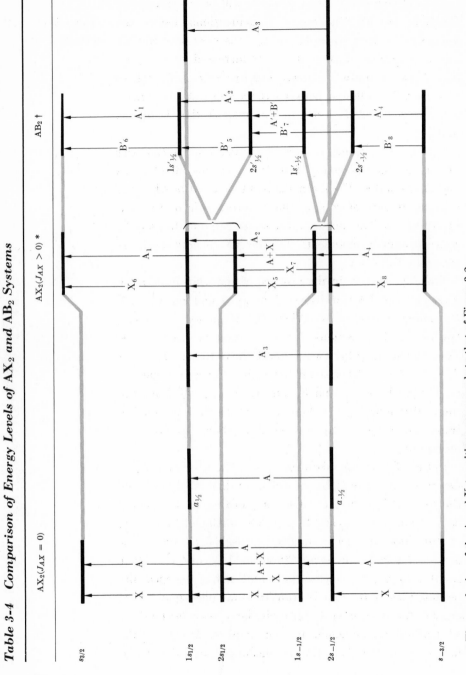

* The numbering of the A and X transitions corresponds to that of Figure 3-2.
† The numbering of the A and B transitions corresponds to that of Figure 3-3.

has the energy ν_A in either AX_2 or AB_2. This transition provides a convenient fixed point for referencing of the other resonances. In the AB_2 system, the transition $1s'_{-1/2} \rightarrow 2s'_{1/2}$ is allowed. In the AX_2 extreme, this transition involves $\alpha\beta\beta \rightarrow \beta\alpha\alpha$, which means that three nuclei change their spins at once. Such transitions are called "combination" transitions and have zero probability both for AX_2 and A_3. Regardless of this, the $A' + B'$ combination is allowed for AB_2, although the transition probability is relatively small.

The nine theoretically possible lines in the AB_2 spectrum can now be assigned to the four different B' transitions, three different A' transitions, the antisymmetric A transition, and the A' + B' combination. The appearance of the

Figure 3-3   Calculated changes in AB_2 spectra with $\nu_A > \nu_B$ and $J_{AB} = 10$ cps as $\nu_A - \nu_B$ changes from 100 to 5 cps at constant ν_A. The positions of ν_A and ν_B are marked for each curve. The dotted lines connect related transitions. The numbering of the transitions is the same as for Table 3-4.

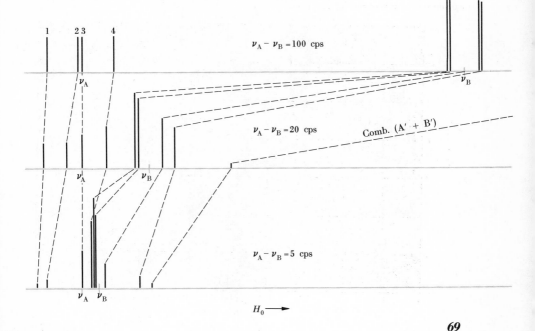

lines changes as shown in Figure 3-3 when $\nu_A - \nu_B$ changes from large to small with respect to J_{AB}. If $\nu_A < \nu_B$, the spectrum will be a mirror image of that shown with the positions of all the lines reversed.

EXERCISE 3-4

Solve the two-row determinants involving the mixing of $1s_{1/2}$ and $2s_{1/2}$ and of $1s_{-1/2}$ and $2s_{-1/2}$ for the AB_2 system for the permitted energy levels. Check your answers by comparing the transition energies calculated for $\nu_A - \nu_B = 20$ cps and $J_{AB} = 10$ cps with the corresponding lines in Figure 3-3.

The changes in the relative energies can very usefully be presented graphically, as in Figure 3-4, as a function of the ratio $J_{AB}/(\nu_A - \nu_B)$. For any given value of the ratio it is only necessary to multiply the relative energy by $\nu_A - \nu_B$ to

Figure 3-4   Calculated changes in relative energies of AB_2 *transitions as a function of* $J_{AB}/(\nu_A - \nu_B)$. *The energy ν of any given transition is obtained by multiplying the appropriate ordinate by $\nu_A - \nu_B$.*

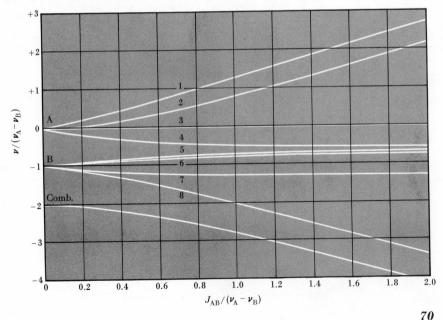

obtain the line positions in cycles per second relative to transition A_3 taken as zero.

The analysis of an AB_2 spectrum is most conveniently
carried out by first locating the position of the antisymmetric
transition A_3, which gives ν_A. The energy ν_B can be obtained
as the mean of the positions of transitions B'_5 and B'_7 since,
as seen from Figure 3-4, the sum of the energies B'_5 and B'_7
is constant. The easiest way to get J_{AB} is by working back-
ward from $\nu_A - \nu_B$ and the various line positions with the
aid of Figure 3-4 or by interpolation in tables of transition
energies as a function of $J_{AB}/(\nu_A - \nu_B)$.[2]

EXERCISE 3-5

Extract ν_A, ν_B, and J_{AB} from the AB_2 spectra shown in
Figure 3-5.

3-3   The ABX *system*

The ABX system is especially significant as the simplest
case involving three different coupling constants where
mixing of states is important. The problem of *determining*
the coupling constants in systems of this type is by no means
trivial. Serious errors in evaluating coupling constants can be
made by simple inspection of spectra involving ABX systems
unless account is taken of the underlying theory of such systems. Thus, for an ABX arrangement such as $-CH{=}CH-$
$\qquad\qquad\qquad\qquad\qquad\qquad\qquad\qquad\qquad$ (B)   (A)
CH—, splitting of the X resonance into a $1:2:1$ triplet might
(X)
be taken as evidence that $J_{AX} = J_{BX}$, even though evidence
from other systems (cf. Section 1-3) indicates that J_{AX}
should be much greater than J_{BX}. The difficulty arises from
the fact that if $J_{AB} \sim (\nu_A - \nu_B) \gg J_{AX}$, then X acts as
though it is coupled with B even when J_{BX} is actually equal to
zero. Another interesting aspect of ABX is that it is the first
system we have seen in which the relative signs of the coupling constants make a difference to the observed spectrum.

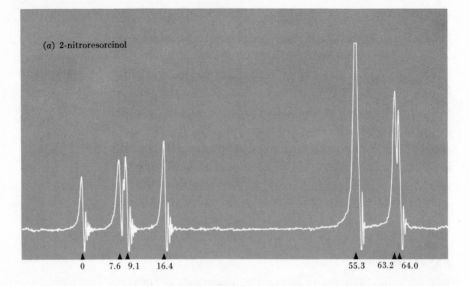

(a) 2-nitroresorcinol

0   7.6 9.1 16.4   55.3   63.2 64.0

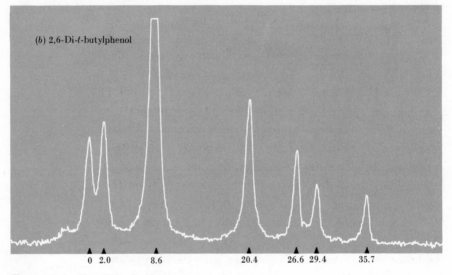

(b) 2,6-Di-t-butylphenol

0 2.0   8.6   20.4   26.6 29.4   35.7

Figure 3-5   Two AB₂ nuclear resonance spectra.

Our starting place will be the AMX energy levels (Table 3-1) for which we shall have ν_A not much larger than ν_M, so as to border on ABX conditions. The energy levels are shown in Table 3-5, first without consideration of spin-spin splitting. For simplicity and definiteness, we shall choose $J_{AM} > J_{AX} \gg J_{MX}$ in taking account of spin-spin splitting. We can see from Table 3-2 that the X transitions have the

Three-Spin Systems

Table 3-5   Comparison of Energy Levels and Transitions of AMX and ABX Systems

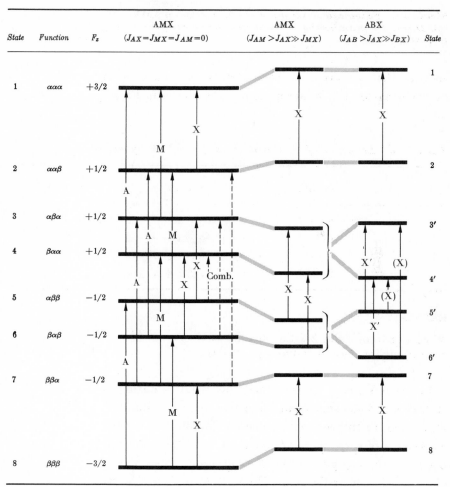

State	Function	F_z	AMX $(J_{AX}=J_{MX}=J_{AM}=0)$	AMX $(J_{AM} > J_{AX} \gg J_{MX})$	ABX $(J_{AB} > J_{AX} \gg J_{BX})$	State
1	$\alpha\alpha\alpha$	$+3/2$				1
2	$\alpha\alpha\beta$	$+1/2$				2
3	$\alpha\beta\alpha$	$+1/2$				3'
4	$\beta\alpha\alpha$	$+1/2$				4'
5	$\alpha\beta\beta$	$-1/2$				5'
6	$\beta\alpha\beta$	$-1/2$				6'
7	$\beta\beta\alpha$	$-1/2$				7
8	$\beta\beta\beta$	$-3/2$				8

73

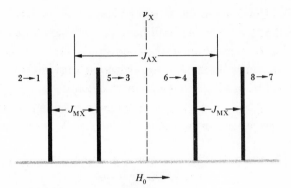

Figure 3-6 *Schematic diagram of the X part of an AMX spectrum. The numbering of the transitions corresponds to that of Table 3-2.*

energies that are given in Table 3-6—so a quartet is to be expected for the X absorptions, as is shown in Figure 3-6.

Table 3-6 *Energies of X Transitions for AMX Systems*

Transition	Energy
$8 \rightarrow 7$	$\nu_X - J_{MX}/2 - J_{AX}/2$
$6 \rightarrow 4$	$\nu_X + J_{MX}/2 - J_{AX}/2$
$5 \rightarrow 3$	$\nu_X - J_{MX}/2 + J_{AX}/2$
$2 \rightarrow 1$	$\nu_X + J_{MX}/2 + J_{AX}/2$

EXERCISE 3-6

Work out from Table 3-2 the energies of the A and M transitions for $J_{MX} = 0$ and $J_{AM} = 2J_{AX}$.

In the ABX case $\nu_A \sim \nu_B$, and this requires mixing of states 3 and 4 and states 5 and 6 to give the mixed states 3′, 4′, 5′, and 6′. Inspection of Table 3-5 reveals that mixing coefficients of these pairs of states are not expected to be equal, so the energies of the X′ transitions 6′ → 4′ and 5′ → 3′ will not be the same. Now, in all, there will be six

X-type transitions. Two of these, $8 \to 7$ and $2 \to 1$, are pure X and unchanged by the mixing of states 3 and 4 and of 5 and 6. Two more are X' transitions, $6' \to 4'$ and $5' \to 3'$, with energies determined by the degree of mixing of the pairs of states. And, finally, there will be two combination transitions, marked (X) in Table 3-5, which are allowed for ABX but not for AMX. These combinations approach pure X transitions as ν_A approaches ν_B, so that we shall expect them to fall in the X region of the spectrum. They are an exception to the rule that combination transitions are usually weak. The combination transition $7 \to 2$ is forbidden over the range of $\nu_A - \nu_B$ for ABX.

Three-Spin Systems

The energy levels for the mixed states are obtained in the usual way. For states 3 and 4, we have the determinant, Equation (3-8).

EXERCISE 3-7

Show that $\langle \alpha\beta\alpha | \mathcal{H} | \beta\alpha\alpha \rangle = J_{AB}/2$.

$$\begin{vmatrix} \begin{matrix}(\nu_A - \nu_B + \nu_X)/2 \\ + (-J_{AB} + J_{AX} - J_{BX})/4 \\ -E\end{matrix} & J_{AB}/2 \\[2ex] J_{AB}/2 & \begin{matrix}(-\nu_A + \nu_B + \nu_X)/2 \\ + (-J_{AB} - J_{AX} + J_{BX})/4 \\ -E\end{matrix} \end{vmatrix} = 0$$

$$(3\text{-}8)$$

Setting $\nu_X/2 - J_{AB}/4 - E = x$, $(\nu_A - \nu_B)/2 + (J_{AX} - J_{BX})/4 = y$ and $J_{AB}/2 = z$, we have

$$\begin{vmatrix} x + y & z \\ z & x - y \end{vmatrix} = x^2 - y^2 - z^2 = 0$$

and hence

$$E = \nu_{\mathrm{X}}/2 - J_{\mathrm{AB}}/4 \pm (1/2)\sqrt{[\nu_{\mathrm{A}} - \nu_{\mathrm{B}} + (J_{\mathrm{AX}} - J_{\mathrm{BX}})/2]^2 + J_{\mathrm{AB}}^2}$$

$$(3\text{-}9)$$

where the plus sign gives E_3' and the minus sign gives E_4'.

EXERCISE 3-8

Derive an expression for E similar to Equation (3-9)
for the mixing of states 5 and 6.

   The X part of the ABX spectrum will be expected schematically to be as shown in Figure 3-7. The difference between $2 \rightarrow 1$ and $8 \rightarrow 7$, which is unaffected by mixing, is $J_{\mathrm{AX}} + J_{\mathrm{BX}}$. An important thing to note is that there is no spacing in the spectrum that corresponds simply to either J_{AX} or J_{BX}. Indeed, although in favorable cases computation of J_{AX} and J_{BX} is relatively straightforward; in others, even though J_{AX} and J_{BX} may have quite different values, these cannot be extracted from the spectrum. The determining factor is the relative magnitude of J_{AB}, $\nu_{\mathrm{A}} - \nu_{\mathrm{B}}$, and $(J_{\mathrm{AX}} - J_{\mathrm{BX}})/2$. If $\nu_{\mathrm{A}} - \nu_{\mathrm{B}}$ and $(J_{\mathrm{AX}} - J_{\mathrm{BX}})/2$ are both small compared with J_{AB}, then only the value of $J_{\mathrm{AX}} + J_{\mathrm{BX}}$ can be obtained. The reason for this may be readily seen from Equation (3-9), which reduces to

*Figure 3-7   Schematic diagram of the X part of an ABX
spectrum. The numbering of the transitions corresponds to
that of Table 3-5.*

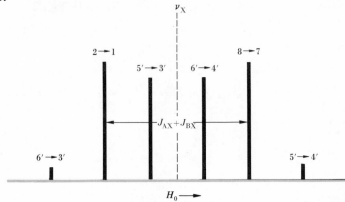

$$E = \nu_X/2 - J_{AB}/4 \pm J_{AB}/2 \qquad\qquad (3\text{-}10)$$

when $J_{AB} \gg \nu_A - \nu_B + (J_{AX} - J_{BX})/2$. In this situation, transitions $6' \to 4'$ and $5' \to 3'$ coincide, the combination transitions $6' \to 3'$ and $5' \to 4'$ are forbidden, and the X part of the spectrum is simplified to a triplet, as shown in Figure 3-8. The spacing $(2 \to 1) - (8 \to 7)$ is $J_{AX} + J_{BX}$ but, of course, either J_{AX} or J_{BX} could even be *zero* without

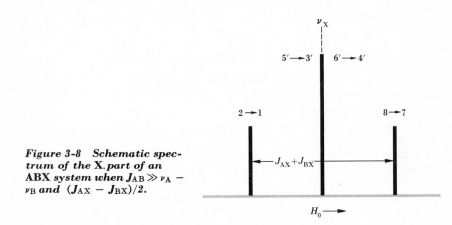

Figure 3-8 Schematic spectrum of the X part of an ABX system when $J_{AB} \gg \nu_A - \nu_B$ and $(J_{AX} - J_{BX})/2$.

affecting the appearance of the spectrum, even though the triplet pattern gives the impression that X is equally coupled to A and B. The message here is that if A and B are tightly coupled with respect to the chemical shift between them, they may act as though they are equally coupled to X.

EXERCISE 3-9

Predict the appearance of the AB part of the ABX spectrum when J_{AB} is much greater than both $\nu_A - \nu_B$ and $(J_{AX} - J_{BX})/2$.

EXERCISE 3-10

The triplet proton resonances observed for the CHBr groups in the A_2X_2 system presented by *trans*-1,2-dibromocyclopropane (I) has been taken as evidence that J_{cis} and J_{trans} are equal. This conclusion might conceivably be tested experimentally in the following way: Consider the ABX system presented by 1-deutero-1,2-dibromocyclopropane (II), which would have the same *cis*- and *trans*-coupling constants as expected for the nondeuterated compound.

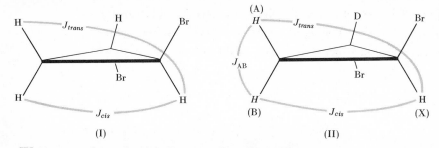

We can neglect the small magnetic effect of the deuterium, or it could be reduced to zero by double resonance.[3] The chemical shift between the hydrogens at the 3-position of the ring should be negligibly small. Suppose that $J_{cis} = 8$ cps and $J_{trans} = 2$ cps, which are reasonably representative values for the angles involved.[4] Now set up the wave functions for this ABX case where $\nu_A \cong \nu_B$ and calculate the positions and intensities of the X resonance lines as a function of J_{AB}. What is your conclusion regarding the value of the use of the monodeutero compound to obtain J_{cis} and J_{trans}? (We shall consider 1,2-dibromocyclopropane as an A_2X_2 case in Chapter 4.)

The AB part of an ABX spectrum consists of two (usually overlapping) quartets, which correspond separately to the two possible values of $I_z(X)$. We can calculate the positions and intensities of the lines of each quartet by considering $J_{AX} \cdot I_z(X)$ and $J_{BX} \cdot I_z(X)$ to effect changes in the chemical shifts of A and B, respectively. With the so-corrected chemical shifts, the usual AB formulas (Section 2-3) apply. The same procedure can be used for the AB spectrum of the general system ABX_n.

EXERCISE 3-11

Calculate the positions and intensities of the AB fluorine resonance lines for the ABX system presented by 1,4-difluoro-2,3,5-trichlorobenzene using the information $J_{FF} = 12$ cps, $J_{HF}(ortho) = 8.4$ cps, $J_{HF}(meta) = 6.3$ cps, and $\Delta\nu = 24.8$ cps.[5]

EXERCISE 3-12

Extract all the information you can from the AB part of the experimental ABX spectrum shown in Figure 3-9.

An interesting aspect of the ABX system is the fact that the appearance of the spectrum depends on the relative signs of J_{AX} and J_{BX} but is independent of the sign of J_{AB}.

EXERCISE 3-13

Show that the appearance of the ABX spectrum will be independent of the sign of J_{AB}.

The line positions are not affected by the relative signs of J_{AX} and J_{BX} but the intensities are. The reasons for this can be seen in the following way: First, we note that the expres-

Figure 3-9 Spectrum given by the AB part of an ABX system.

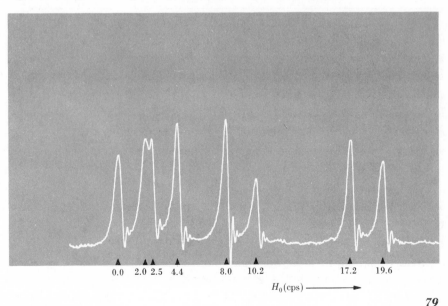

H_0(cps) ⟶

0.0   2.0 2.5   4.4   8.0   10.2   17.2   19.6

sions for the energy of states 3′ and 4′ [Equation (3-9) and Exercise 3-8] contain the term

$$D_+ = (1/2)\sqrt{[(\nu_A - \nu_B) + (J_{AX} - J_{BX})/2]^2 + J_{AB}{}^2} \qquad (3\text{-}11)$$

while those for 5′ and 6′ include

$$D_- = (1/2)\sqrt{[(\nu_A - \nu_B) - (J_{AX} - J_{BX})/2]^2 + J_{AB}{}^2} \qquad (3\text{-}12)$$

Now, if we consider the X transitions shown in Table 3-5, we find that their energies are those given in Table 3-7. Transitions $2 \to 1$ and $8 \to 7$ are in order of decreasing energy if

Table 3-7   Energies of X Transitions for ABX Systems

Transition	Energy
$6' \to 3'$	$\nu_X + D_+ + D_-$
$2 \to 1$	$\nu_X + (J_{AX} + J_{BX})/2$
$5' \to 3'$	$\nu_X + D_+ - D_-$
$6' \to 4'$	$\nu_X - D_+ + D_-$
$8 \to 7$	$\nu_X - (J_{AX} + J_{BX})/2$
$5' \to 4'$	$\nu_X - D_+ - D_-$

$J_{AX} + J_{BX}$ is positive and $J_{AX} > J_{BX}$, so that $J_{AX} - J_{BX}$ is positive. If the signs of J_{AX} and J_{BX} are both reversed, the transitions change places in the scale but their energies remain the same. Thus, whether $2 \to 1$ or $8 \to 7$ has the lowest energy depends on the sign of $(J_{AX} + J_{BX})$; but since the two transitions are identical in so far as observables are concerned, we cannot tell them apart. Therefore, it is not possible to find the absolute signs of J_{AX} and J_{BX}.

However, consider now a specific value of $|J_{AX} + J_{BX}|$ = 10 cps. This would be observed as the separation between transitions $2 \to 1$ and $8 \to 7$. Such a 10-cps separation could, of course, come about as the result of combinations of coupling constants with the same or opposite signs; such as $J_{AX} = 15$, $J_{BX} = -5$, and $J_{AX} = 5$, $J_{BX} = 5$. The combinations of this sort that are possible can be determined from the split between transitions $5' \to 3'$ and $6' \to 4'$, which is $2(D_+ - D_-)$, and that between $6' \to 3'$ and $5' \to 4'$, which is $2(D_+ + D_-)$.

$$2(D_+ - D_-) = E_{5' \to 3'} - E_{6' \to 4'}$$
$$2(D_+ + D_-) = E_{6' \to 3'} - E_{5' \to 4'}$$
(3-13)

Since D_+ and D_- are both positive, $2(D_+ + D_-)$ is positive, but $2(D_+ - D_-)$ can be either positive or negative. For convenience, let us define quantities c_1 and c_2 such that

$$c_1 = |E_{5' \to 3'} - E_{6' \to 4'}|$$
$$c_2 = E_{6' \to 3'} - E_{5' \to 4'}$$
(3-14)

Now we can write

$$2(D_+ - D_-) = \pm c_1 \tag{3-15}$$

$$2(D_+ + D_-) = c_2 \tag{3-16}$$

$$D_+ = (c_2 \pm c_1)/4 \tag{3-17}$$

$$D_- = (c_2 \mp c_1)/4 \tag{3-18}$$

Equations (3-11) and (3-12) can be rewritten as

$$\nu_A - \nu_B + (J_{AX} - J_{BX})/2 = \pm \sqrt{4D_+^2 - J_{AB}^2} \tag{3-19}$$

$$\nu_A - \nu_B - (J_{AX} - J_{BX})/2 = \pm \sqrt{4D_-^2 - J_{AB}^2} \tag{3-20}$$

If we take all possible combinations of the algebraic signs of the right halves of the simultaneous equations (3-19) and (3-20), we can solve for the possible sets of values of $\nu_A - \nu_B$, J_{AX}, and J_{BX} in terms of the observables: c_1, c_2, $|J_{AX} + J_{BX}|$, and J_{AB} (from the AB spectrum).

EXERCISE 3-14

Derive the relationships

$$(J_{AX} - J_{BX})/2 = \pm c_1 c_2 / [4(\nu_A - \nu_B)]$$

and

$$(J_{AX} - J_{BX})/2 = \pm [(c_1^2 + c_2^2)/4 - (\nu_A - \nu_B)^2 - J_{AB}^2]^{1/2}$$

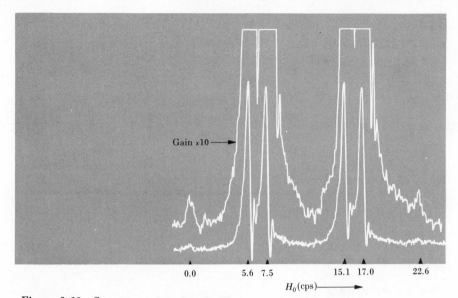

Gain x10 ——→

0.0   5.6 7.5   15.1 17.0   22.6

H_0(cps)——→

*Figure 3-10   Spectrum given by the X part of an ABX system,
here the 60-Mc fluorine resonances of 2-fluoro-4,6-dibromo-
phenol dissolved in carbon tetrachloride. The values of
J_{AB} and $(J_{AX} + J_{BX})$ obtained from the AB part of the
spectrum are 2.4 and 7.4 cps, respectively.*

starting from Equations (3-15) and (3-16). These re-
lations may be found useful in testing the consistency of
experimentally measured separations of ABX patterns.

EXERCISE 3-15

Calculate the sets of $\nu_A - \nu_B$ and coupling constants
J_{AX} and J_{BX}, which fit the X part of the ABX spectrum shown in Figure 3-10. Be sure each of your sets
gives the proper line spacings for the spectrum.

A decision between the possible sets of coupling constants
may be obtained by investigation of the theoretical intensities for the transitions involving mixed states (the transitions $2 \to 1$ and $8 \to 7$ each have unit probability). We
shall be illustrative rather than comprehensive in the
matter, as a complete analysis is rather laborious. [5] It will be
convenient to compare the intensities of the transitions
$6' \to 3'$ and $5' \to 3'$. To do this we must compute mixing

82

coefficients for the states 3 and 4 and for 5 and 6. Let these be a and b for states 3 and 4 and p and q for states 5 and 6. Thus, we can write

$$\Psi_{3'} = (a\alpha\beta + b\beta\alpha)\alpha \tag{3-21}$$
$$\Psi_{4'} = (b\alpha\beta - a\beta\alpha)\alpha \tag{3-22}$$
$$\Psi_{5'} = (p\alpha\beta + q\beta\alpha)\beta \tag{3-23}$$
$$\Psi_{6'} = (q\alpha\beta - p\beta\alpha)\beta \tag{3-24}$$

where $a^2 + b^2 = 1$ and $p^2 + q^2 = 1$ by the normalization condition.

The transition probabilities can be computed by the previously described procedure [Section 2-2, particularly Equation (2-18)].

$$
\begin{aligned}
P_{5'\to 3'} &= [\langle(a\alpha\beta + b\beta\alpha)\alpha \,|\, F_+ \,|\, (p\alpha\beta + q\beta\alpha)\beta\rangle]^2 \\
&= (ap\langle\alpha\beta\alpha\,|\,\alpha\beta\alpha\rangle + bq\langle\beta\alpha\alpha\,|\,\beta\alpha\alpha\rangle)^2 \\
&= (ap + bq)^2
\end{aligned} \tag{3-25}
$$

$$
\begin{aligned}
P_{6'\to 3'} &= [\langle(a\alpha\beta + b\beta\alpha)\alpha \,|\, F_+ \,|\, (q\alpha\beta - p\beta\alpha)\beta\rangle]^2 \\
&= (aq - bp)^2
\end{aligned} \tag{3-26}
$$

$$P_{5'\to 3'}/P_{6'\to 3'} = (ap + bq)^2/(aq - bp)^2 \tag{3-27}$$

This equation is more convenient if cast in terms of a/b and p/q, since then the normalized coefficients are not necessary.

Figure 3-11   Theoretical line positions and intensities for the X part of an ABX system with J_{AX} and J_{BX} having opposite signs.

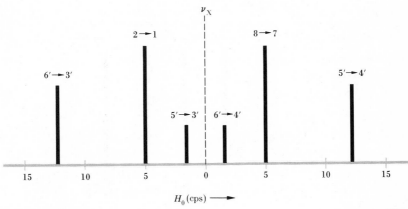

$$P_{5'\to 3'}/P_{6'\to 3'} = [1 + (ap/bq)]^2/[(a/b) - (p/q)]^2 \qquad (3\text{-}28)$$

Values of a/b and p/q are obtained as usual by taking ratios of cofactors:

$$a/b = [(-\nu_A + \nu_B)/2 - (J_{AX} - J_{BX})/4 - D_+]/(-J_{AB}/2) \qquad (3\text{-}29)$$

$$p/q = [(-\nu_A + \nu_B)/2 + (J_{AX} - J_{BX})/4 - D_-]/(-J_{AB}/2) \qquad (3\text{-}30)$$

EXERCISE 3-16

Derive Equations (3-29) and (3-30) from Equations (3-8) and (3-9) and the results of Exercise 3-8.

To illustrate the behavior of intensities with the two sets of coupling constants, we shall use a case with $J_{AB} = 7$ cps and $J_{AX} = +15$ cps, $J_{BX} = -5$ cps and $\nu_A - \nu_B = +2$ cps, or $J_{AX} = +7$ cps, $J_{BX} = +3$ cps, and $\nu_A - \nu_B = 10$ cps. When J_{AX} and J_{BX} have opposite signs, the spectrum is as shown in Figure 3-11 with the intensity of $6' \to 3'$ greater than $5' \to 3'$. With J_{AX} and J_{BX} having the same sign, the appearance of the spectrum changes drastically and $6' \to 3'$ becomes much less intense than $5' \to 3'$ (Figure 3-12). In this case we can make an unambiguous assignment of the relative signs by analysis of the relative intensities.

Figure 3-12 Theoretical line positions and intensities for the system shown in Figure 3-11 but with J_{AX} and J_{BX} having the same relative signs.

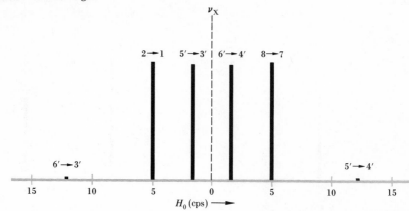

Determine the proper relative signs of J_{AX} and J_{BX} for the spectrum treated in Exercise 3-15. Take $\nu_A <$ ν_B and $J_{AX} > J_{BX}$.

Three-Spin Systems

EXERCISE 3-18

Calculate the appearance of the AB part of the ABX spectrum with the J_{AX} and J_{BX} coupling constants having the same and opposite signs for the case given in Exercise 3-17.

Several other examples of the analysis of ABX spectra, including determination of the relative signs of the coupling constants, have been discussed by Gutowsky, Holm, Saika, and Williams. [5]

3-4 *The ABC system*

Treatment of an ABC system by the variation method is straightforward right down to the point where solutions of three-row determinants like Equation (3-31) for $F_z = 1/2$ are necessary. It is difficult to solve Equation (3-31) and the corresponding determinant for $F_z = -1/2$ to obtain the final energy levels and wave functions in explicit analytical form. However, solution of these determinants for particular values of the parameters is not at all difficult and, at worst, is only laborious.

EXERCISE 3-19

Calculate the fifteen transition energies for the ABC system presented by a vinyl compound (III),

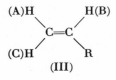

(III)

$$\begin{vmatrix} (\nu_A + \nu_B - \nu_C)/2 \\ + (J_{AB} - J_{BC} - J_{AC})/4 \\ -E & J_{BC}/2 & J_{AC}/2 \\[2ex] J_{BC}/2 & \begin{matrix}(\nu_A - \nu_B + \nu_C)/2 \\ + (-J_{AB} - J_{BC} + J_{AC})/4 \\ -E\end{matrix} & J_{AB}/2 \\[2ex] J_{AC}/2 & J_{AB}/2 & \begin{matrix}(-\nu_A + \nu_B + \nu_C)/2 \\ + (-J_{AB} + J_{BC} - J_{AC})/4 \\ -E\end{matrix} \end{vmatrix} = 0 \qquad (3\text{-}31)$$

86

with $J_{AB} = 12$ cps, $J_{BC} = 20$ cps, and $J_{AC} = 0$. Set $\nu_A = 0$ as a reference point and use $\nu_A - \nu_B = 6$ cps, $\nu_A - \nu_C = 10$ cps, so that $\nu_B - \nu_C = 4$ cps.

The usual way to analyze the resonances of the ABC system is to guess the parameters as closely as possible from related substances and to use an electronic computer to obtain theoretical spectra to compare with the experimental spectrum. An excellent example of this procedure has been provided by Johnson, Weiner, Waugh, and Seyferth [6] for the ABC spectrum given by vinyllithium. Here, the computer readout was coupled to an oscilloscope so that a visual display of the theoretical energies and intensities could be compared directly with experiment (see Figure 3-13).

Figure 3-13   Comparison of experimental and theoretical spectra of the ABC system provided by vinyllithium. The upper curve is the experimental spectrum and the lower curve is a photograph of the trace produced by coupling a computer output of calculated line positions and intensities to an oscilloscope.[6] (Courtesy of J. S. Waugh.)

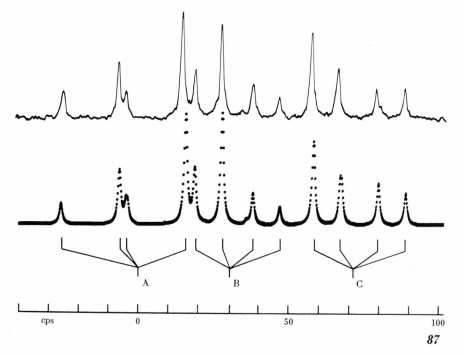

References

1. J. D. Roberts, "Nuclear Magnetic Resonance. Applications to Organic Chemistry," McGraw-Hill Book Company, Inc., New York, 1959, pp. 48–49.
2. J. A. Pople, W. G. Schneider, and H. J. Bernstein, "High-resolution Nuclear Magnetic Resonance," McGraw-Hill Book Company, Inc., 1959, p. 127.
3. Ref. 1, p. 86.
4. L. M. Jackman, "Applications of Nuclear Magnetic Resonance Spectroscopy in Organic Chemistry," Pergamon Press, New York, 1959, p. 87.
5. H. S. Gutowsky, C. H. Holm, A. Saika, and G. A. Williams, *J. Am. Chem. Soc.*, **79**, 4596 (1957).
6. C. S. Johnson, Jr., M. A. Weiner, J. S. Waugh, and D. Seyferth, *J. Am. Chem. Soc.*, **83**, 1306 (1961).

THE NUMBER of possible classes, such as A_4, AX_3, ABX_2, and $ABCD$, that can be made up of various combinations of four spins is quite large. Comparative analyses of these are far beyond the scope of this book. With the advent of high-speed-computer programs to permit comparison of theoretical and experimental spectra for seven or more spins, the practical problems presented by four-spin systems are readily soluble, particularly if effective use can also be made of double-resonance, spectral moments, and isotopic substitution.[1] One important theoretical point that can only be illustrated by at least a four-spin system is that, in appropriate circumstances, more resonance lines may appear than might be predicted simply, even if the chemical shift is *infinitely large* with respect to the coupling constants. The reason for this possibility will now be discussed, using the A_2X_2 system as an example.

EXERCISE 4-1

Classify the following molecules by the kind of four-spin system they are expected to present—A_3B, etc.:

  a. Fluoroform
  b. 1,2-Dichlorobenzene
  c. 1,3-Dichlorobenzene
  d. 1-Bromo-2-chlorotetrafluoroethane

e.

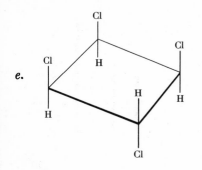

f. 1-Phenyl-4-chlorocyclobutene

g.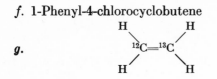

4-1   The A_2X_2 system

There are two possible types of A_2X_2 arrangements. These differ in the average orientation of the A_2 pair with respect to the X_2 pair so there is either one AX coupling constant or two. Examples are 1,1-difluoroethylene (I) with two AX coupling constants and 1,1-difluoroallene (II) with one AX coupling constant. We shall arbitrarily take H as A and F as X in the following discussion.

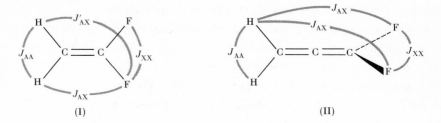

(I)   (II)

The A_2X_2 systems with a single AX coupling constant can easily be shown to give rise to symmetrical (1:2:1) triplet resonances for A and X with spacings equal to J_{AX}. The

Figure 4-1   Schematic (and incorrect) resonance spectrum for protons of 1,1-difluoroethylene based on consideration of formulas (III) through (VI) with $J_{HF} \neq J'_{HF}$. The two outer lines are here ascribed to (III) and (IV), respectively, and the inner quartet to (V) and (VI).

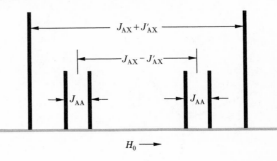

values of J_{AA} and J_{XX} do not affect the spectrum. The A_2X_2 cases with two coupling constants J_{AX} and J'_{AX} are more interesting and will be discussed in detail since, in general, ten different resonance lines will be observed for each nucleus. This is highly significant because from simple considerations it is hard to see how more than six lines can result. Thus, for difluoroethylene, we might naively expect four species [(III) through (VI)] to be present in a ratio of 1:1:1:1; (III) and (IV) could give single separate proton resonances, while (V) and (VI) could give two identical and

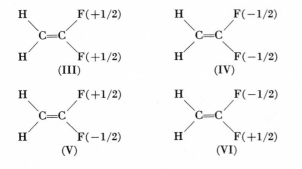

Figure 4-2 Proton spectrum of 1,1-difluoroethylene at 60 Mc.

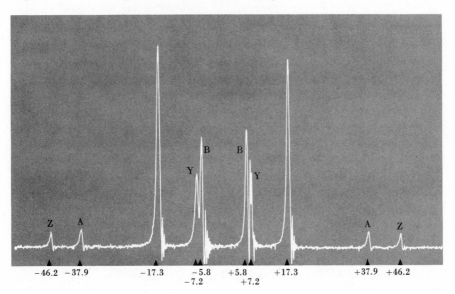

coinciding quartets as might befit protons rendered non-equivalent by virtue of the magnetic effects exerted by the *cis* and *trans* fluorines. The resulting proton spectrum could look something like that shown in Figure 4-1. However, we should be immediately suspicious of this naive analysis because it involves assigning explicit I_z values to each of the equivalent fluorines in (V) and (VI) to violate the principles

Table 4-1   Basic Wave Functions for A_2X_2 *Systems*

State	F_z	Symbol	Function
1	$+2$	s_2	$\alpha\alpha\alpha\alpha$
2	$+1$	$1s_1$	$(1/\sqrt{2})(\alpha\beta + \beta\alpha)\alpha\alpha$
3	$+1$	$2s_1$	$\alpha\alpha(1/\sqrt{2})(\alpha\beta + \beta\alpha)$
4	$+1$	$1a_1$	$(1/\sqrt{2})(\alpha\beta - \beta\alpha)\alpha\alpha$
5	$+1$	$2a_1$	$\alpha\alpha(1/\sqrt{2})(\alpha\beta - \beta\alpha)$
6	0	$1s_0$	$\beta\beta\alpha\alpha$
7	0	$2s_0$	$\alpha\alpha\beta\beta$
8	0	$3s_0$	$(1/2)(\alpha\beta - \beta\alpha)\,(\alpha\beta - \beta\alpha)$ *
9	0	$4s_0$	$(1/2)(\alpha\beta + \beta\alpha)\,(\alpha\beta + \beta\alpha)$ *
10	0	$1a_0$	$(1/2)(\alpha\beta + \beta\alpha)\,(\alpha\beta - \beta\alpha)$ *
11	0	$2a_0$	$(1/2)(\alpha\beta - \beta\alpha)\,(\alpha\beta + \beta\alpha)$ *
12	-1	$1s_{-1}$	$(1/\sqrt{2})(\alpha\beta + \beta\alpha)\beta\beta$
13	-1	$2s_{-1}$	$\beta\beta(1/\sqrt{2})(\alpha\beta + \beta\alpha)$
14	-1	$1a_{-1}$	$(1/\sqrt{2})(\alpha\beta - \beta\alpha)\beta\beta$
15	-1	$2a_{-1}$	$\beta\beta(1/\sqrt{2})(\alpha\beta - \beta\alpha)$
16	-2	s_{-2}	$\beta\beta\beta\beta$

* These functions are seen to be appropriately symmetric (or anti-symmetric) if the numberings within the pairs of nuclei 1,2 and 3,4 are interchanged simultaneously.

discussed in Section 2-2. Furthermore, the observed proton spectrum of 1,1-difluoroethylene is quite different, as can be seen from Figure 4-2. Indeed, all ten of the resonance lines appear that are predicted by the complete analysis.

Analysis of the A_2X_2 system requires the usual consideration of basic wave functions and the possibility of mixing of states. The basic functions will include products of pairs of symmetric and antisymmetric wave functions set up separately for the A_2 and X_2 nuclei. The basic wave functions for A_2X_2 systems are listed in Table 4-1. The notation generally follows that of Pople, Schneider, and Bernstein.[2]

It will be necessary to consider only the A transitions, since the X pattern is identical except for the fact that it is centered on ν_X instead of ν_A. For convenience, we shall analyze the antisymmetric energy levels separately from the symmetric energy levels. This is theoretically satisfactory since all $a \rightarrow s$ transitions are forbidden, and it offers practical advantages as a place to start because the number of antisymmetric states is relatively smaller. Table 4-2 lists the basic antisymmetric energy levels for the A_2X_2 system. To provide further simplification the following conventions introduced by McConnell, McLean, and Reilly[3] are employed:

$$J_{AA} + J_{XX} = K \qquad J_{AX} - J'_{AX} = L$$
$$J_{AA} - J_{XX} = M \qquad J_{AX} + J'_{AX} = N \tag{4-1}$$

EXERCISE 4-2

Verify that the energies of the $2a_1$ and $2a_0$ states are those given in Table 4-2.

Table 4-2   Basic Antisymmetric Wave Functions for A_2X_2 *Systems*

State	Symbol	Function	Energy
4	$1a_1$	$(1/\sqrt{2})\,(\alpha\beta - \beta\alpha)\alpha\alpha$	$\nu_X - K/4 - M/2$
5	$2a_1$	$\alpha\alpha(1/\sqrt{2})\,(\alpha\beta - \beta\alpha)$	$\nu_A - K/4 + M/2$
10	$1a_0$	$(1/2)\,(\alpha\beta + \beta\alpha)\,(\alpha\beta - \beta\alpha)$	$-K/4 + M/2$
11	$2a_0$	$(1/2)\,(\alpha\beta - \beta\alpha)\,(\alpha\beta + \beta\alpha)$	$-K/4 - M/2$
14	$1a_{-1}$	$(1/\sqrt{2})\,(\alpha\beta - \beta\alpha)\beta\beta$	$-\nu_X - K/4 - M/2$
15	$2a_{-1}$	$\beta\beta(1/\sqrt{2})\,(\alpha\beta - \beta\alpha)$	$-\nu_A - K/4 + M/2$

A Four-Spin System. A_2X_2

Since all the antisymmetric states include the constant term $-K/4$, this can be omitted; we then have energy levels as shown in Table 4-3, using for convenience $\nu_A > \nu_X$, as we

Table 4-3   *Antisymmetric Energy Levels and A-Type Transitions for A_2X_2 Systems*

State	$M = 0$	$M > 0, L = 0$	$M > 0, L \neq 0$	State
$2a_1$				$2a_1$
$1a_1$		A	A'	$1a_1$
	A	A	A'	$1a_0'$
$1a_0, 2a_0$	A	A	A'	$2a_0'$
$1a_{-1}$	A	A	A'	$1a_{-1}$
$2a_{-1}$				$2a_{-1}$

have in dealing with AX_2, etc. (cf. Table 3-4). (Only A transitions are shown in the table.) If $M = 0$, and we assume no mixing of states, then four equal A transitions would be expected. If $M > 0$, and again we assume no mixing, the four A transitions should have the energies $\nu_A + M$, ν_A, ν_A, and $\nu_A - M$. Actually, unless the absolute value of M is very large with respect to the other coupling constants, we expect that the states $1a_0$ and $2a_0$ would mix.

EXERCISE 4-3

Calculate the probabilities for each of the A transitions $2a_{-1} \rightarrow 1a_0$, $2a_{-1} \rightarrow 2a_0$, etc., as correspond to the

94

middle group in Table 4-3 with $M > 0$ and $L = 0$ (no mixing).

The energies and wave functions for the states $1a_0'$ and $2a_0'$ that result from mixing of $1a_0$ and $2a_0$ are easily calculated by the procedures used previously. The secular determinant for $\psi = c_1\psi_{1a_0} + c_2\psi_{2a_0}$ is as follows:

$$\begin{vmatrix} M/2 - E & -L/2 \\ -L/2 & -M/2 - E \end{vmatrix} = 0 \tag{4-2}$$

and

$$E = \pm (1/2)\sqrt{M^2 + L^2} \tag{4-3}$$

EXERCISE 4-4

Verify that the off-diagonal matrix element of Equation (4-2) is $-L/2$.

From Equation (4-3) we see that, if L is small compared to M, the energy levels are expected to be as shown in the second column of Table 4-3 and the transition probabilities as calculated in Exercise 4-3.

EXERCISE 4-5

Derive an expression for the mixing coefficients of ψ_{1a_0} and ψ_{2a_0} in terms of M and L. From this expression set up an equation for the ratio of the intensities of the transitions $2a_0' \rightarrow 2a_1$ and $1a_0' \rightarrow 2a_1$.

The energies of the transitions between the A antisymmetric states are found from Equation (4-3) and Table 4-3. They fall as shown in Table 4-4 when $M > 0$. In the case of 1,1-difluoroethylene these transitions constitute two pairs of lines in the observed spectrum (Figure 4-2). It cannot be determined from the spectrum alone whether or not these pairs are the resonances marked A, A and B, B or Y, Y, or else Z, Z and B, B or Y, Y; however, on the basis of data from related compounds, one pair of antisymmetric transitions is believed to be A, A.[3] In any event, the important thing to note is that if $L > 0$, then four resonance lines appear as the result of mixing of the antisymmetric states.

Table 4-4   Energies of Antisymmetric A_2X_2 Transitions

Transition	Energy
$2a_0' \rightarrow 2a_1$	$\nu_A + M/2 + (M^2 + L^2)^{1/2}/2$
$2a_{-1} \rightarrow 1a_0'$	$\nu_A - M/2 + (M^2 + L^2)^{1/2}/2$
$1a_0' \rightarrow 2a_1$	$\nu_A + M/2 - (M^2 + L^2)^{1/2}/2$
$2a_{-1} \rightarrow 2a_0'$	$\nu_A - M/2 - (M^2 + L^2)^{1/2}/2$

The behavior of the antisymmetric A lines of an A_2X_2 spectrum as a function of M and L is helpful as an aid to what one can safely deduce about the relative magnitudes of the coupling constants J_{AX} and J'_{AX} without a detailed analysis. Consider L to decrease and become small compared to M. When this happens the transitions $1a_0' \rightarrow 2a_1$ and $2a_{-1} \rightarrow 1a_0'$ tend to become more probable and equal in energy. Indeed, when L is zero, these transitions become part of the central line of the resulting A triplet—the outside lines arising from transitions between symmetric states. Thus, the separation of the first pair of lines centered on ν_A represents a minimum value of $-M + (M^2 + L^2)^{1/2}$. It has to be a minimum because this pair of lines could also result from symmetric transitions.

EXERCISE 4-6

Consider again the case of *trans*-1,2-dibromocyclopropane that was discussed in Exercise 3-10, this time as an A_2X_2 system. Let the CH_2 group be A_2 and the 1,2-hydrogens, X_2 (VII).

Let us assume that $J_{AX}(cis) = 8$ cps and $J'_{AX}(trans)$ = 2 cps, which are reasonable values for the angles involved. It will be appropriate to set J_{XX} as 2 cps because it is a *trans* coupling like J'_{AX}. Now calculate the minimum value of J_{AA}, which will prevent the transition energies of $2a_{-1} \rightarrow 1a'_0$ and $1a'_0 \rightarrow 2a_1$ from being separated by more than 1 cps. It should be clear from this exercise that it is far from true to consider that spectra of systems of the A_2X_2 type are independent of J_{AA} and J_{XX} when $J_{AX} \neq J'_{AX}$.

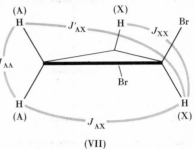

(VII)

The treatment of the symmetric transitions of the A_2X_2 system with $J_{AX} \neq J'_{AX}$ is relatively complicated because there are ten states involved; but since no new principles are involved we shall forge ahead along the lines used for the antisymmetric transitions. The energies of the basic symmetric states are given in Table 4-5 and are represented

Table 4-5 Basic Symmetric Functions and Energies for A_2X_2 Systems

State	Symbol	Function	Energy
1	s_2	$\alpha\alpha\alpha\alpha$	$\nu_A + \nu_X + N/2 + K/4$
2	$1s_1$	$(1/\sqrt{2})(\alpha\beta + \beta\alpha)\alpha\alpha$	$\nu_X + K/4$
3	$2s_1$	$\alpha\alpha(1/\sqrt{2})(\alpha\beta + \beta\alpha)$	$\nu_A + K/4$
6	$1s_0$	$\beta\beta\alpha\alpha$	$-\nu_A + \nu_X - N/2 + K/4$
7	$2s_0$	$\alpha\alpha\beta\beta$	$\nu_A - \nu_X - N/2 + K/4$
8	$3s_0$	$(1/2)(\alpha\beta - \beta\alpha)(\alpha\beta - \beta\alpha)$	$-3K/4$
9	$4s_0$	$(1/2)(\alpha\beta + \beta\alpha)(\alpha\beta + \beta\alpha)$	$+K/4$
12	$1s_{-1}$	$(1/\sqrt{2})(\alpha\beta + \beta\alpha)\beta\beta$	$-\nu_X + K/4$
13	$2s_{-1}$	$\beta\beta(1/\sqrt{2})(\alpha\beta + \beta\alpha)$	$-\nu_A + K/4$
16	s_{-2}	$\beta\beta\beta\beta$	$-\nu_A - \nu_X + N/2 + K/4$

Table 4-6 Symmetric Energy Levels and A-Type Transitions for A_2X_2 Systems

State	$K, N, L = 0$	$K, N > 0, L = 0$	$K, N, L > 0$	State

schematically in Table 4-6. To make Table 4-6 less cumbersome, $K/4$ is subtracted from each energy level and only the A transitions are shown.

EXERCISE 4-7

Verify the energies given in Table 4-5 for s_2, $1s_1$, and $3s_0$.

98

EXERCISE 4-8

Show that the transition probabilities for the A transitions represented with dashed lines in the first and second columns of Table 4-6 are forbidden. Predict the line positions for the symmetric transitions shown in the second column of Table 4-6.

A Four-Spin System. A_2X_2

Inspection of the second column of Table 4-6 shows that unless K is very large, account must be taken of mixing of states $3s_0$ and $4s_0$ to give two new states $3s_0'$ and $4s_0'$. The degree of mixing is easily calculated by the determinant (4-4), which represents the variation treatment of $c_1\psi_{3s_0} + c_2\psi_{4s_0}$ ($K/4$ being subtracted from each of the diagonal matrix elements).

$$\begin{vmatrix} -K - E & -L/2 \\ -L/2 & -E \end{vmatrix} = 0 \qquad (4\text{-}4)$$

and

$$E = (-K \pm \sqrt{K^2 + L^2})/2 \qquad (4\text{-}5)$$

EXERCISE 4-9

Verify that the off-diagonal matrix element of Equation (4-4) is $-L/2$.

Table 4-7   Energies of Symmetric A_2X_2 Transitions

Transition	Energy
$3s_0' \rightarrow 2s_1$	$\nu_A + (K + \sqrt{K^2 + L^2})/2$
$1s_1 \rightarrow s_2$	$\nu_A + N/2$
$1s_0 \rightarrow 1s_1$	$\nu_A + N/2$
$2s_{-1} \rightarrow 4s_0'$	$\nu_A + (-K + \sqrt{K^2 + L^2})/2$
$4s_0' \rightarrow 2s_1$	$\nu_A + (K - \sqrt{K^2 + L^2})/2$
$1s_{-1} \rightarrow 2s_0$	$\nu_A - N/2$
$s_{-2} \rightarrow 1s_{-1}$	$\nu_A - N/2$
$2s_{-1} \rightarrow 3s_0'$	$\nu_A + (-K - \sqrt{K^2 + L^2})/2$

The mixing of states $3s_0$ and $4s_0$ makes the transitions $3s_0' \to 2s_1$ and $2s_{-1} \to 3s_0'$ allowed, although with low transition probabilities. At the same time, the equal transitions $2s_{-1} \to 4s_0$ and $4s_0 \to 2s_1$ become $2s_{-1} \to 4s_0'$ and $4s_0' \to 2s_1$, with different energies. Thus, four lines result from one through mixing. In all, there will be eight symmetric transitions, four of which coincide in two pairs. These will come as given in Table 4-7 if $K > 0$.

The relative intensities of these transitions can easily be calculated in the usual way.

EXERCISE 4-10

McConnell, McLean, and Reilly [3] give the following coupling constants for 1,1-difluoroethylene:

$J_{HH} \approx 4$ cps $J_{HF}(trans) \approx 34$ cps

$J_{FF} \approx 37$ cps $J_{HF}(cis) \approx 1$ cps

These coupling constants were obtained from a spectrum at relatively lower resolution than recently available. Figure 4-2 is a calibrated high-resolution proton spectrum of 1,1-difluoroethylene at 60 Mc. Using the

Figure 4-3 *Proton spectrum of the 3,5-aromatic hydrogens of p-nitrophenol at 60 Mc.*

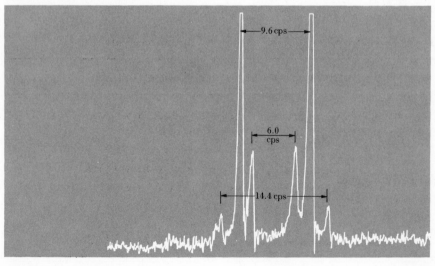

previously assigned values as a basis for argument, determine a more refined set of coupling constants. Compare the calculated and observed intensities.

EXERCISE 4-11

The calibrated spectrum of Figure 4-3 is of the 3,5-aromatic protons of *p*-nitrophenol at 60 Mc. The spectrum very closely approximates A_2X_2, and the 2,6-protons give a set of resonance lines that are a mirror image of those shown in Figure 4-3. Compute a set of coupling constants that fit with the observed line positions. Assume, as has been found with other similar systems, that the 2,5 and 3,6 couplings are zero.

References

1. See J. A. Pople, W. G. Schneider, and H. J. Bernstein, "High-resolution Nuclear Magnetic Resonance," McGraw-Hill Book Company, Inc., New York, 1959, pp. 156–164, for references and discussion.
2. Ref. 1, pp. 139–142.
3. H. M. McConnell, A. D. McLean, and C. A. Reilly, *J. Chem. Phys.*, **23**, 1152 (1955).

ALTHOUGH the present book is intended only to be an introduction to the principles used in the analysis of complex nuclear magnetic resonance spectra, it may not be out of place to comment briefly on the important problems and possible future trends in the field. We have seen that direct analysis of nuclear magnetic resonance spectra of systems of as few as even three or four nuclei with spin 1/2 may be a far from simple task. However, high-speed-computer programs permit the calculation of transition energies and probabilities corresponding to particular chemical-shift and coupling parameters for systems of seven or more nuclei, so that by trial and error one can achieve any desired degree of correspondence between calculation and experiment.

It remains to be demonstrated how practical and satisfactory this approach really is. Practicality will probably be determined to a considerable degree by the development of convenient electrical or mechanical means for converting computer readout to visual display in order to permit precise interpolation between calculated and observed line positions and intensities. The ultimate extent of satisfaction with the trial-and-error method may well hinge on the uniqueness of parameters to which a given spectrum can be said to correspond. It is already clear for the degree of resolution now attainable that a nuclear resonance spectrum, which is less complex than it could be for the number of spins involved, *cannot* always be safely taken as the expression of one and only one set of chemical-shift and coupling parameters.* How frequently this situation will arise with spec-

* See the discussion on p. 77 of the conditions for observation of a triplet X resonance for an ABX system when $J_{AX} \neq J_{BX}$.

tra of normal complexity probably only can be determined through intensive experience.

The lack of aesthetic pleasure associated with use of the trial-and-error approach may be expected to lead to more work on the development of efficient computer programs for the analysis of spectra that would give directly the corresponding shift and coupling parameters. At least, we can expect to see more general analytical procedures analogous to those used in determination of structures by x-ray and electron diffraction.* The fact that the output of NMR spectrometers is particularly suitable for recording on magnetic tape might greatly facilitate direct and precise electronic computation of spectral moments [W. A. Anderson and H. M. McConnell, *J. Chem. Phys.*, **26**, 1496 (1957)], which moments would be very helpful in at least the preliminary analysis of complex spectra. The use of ^{13}C and ^{2}H as aids to the analysis of proton spectra of organic molecules is well known and is capable of considerable expansion. Decoupling of proton spins by double resonance also has great promise for simplification of complex proton spectra and may be expected to become employed more widely as the result of the development of practical electronic equipment for this purpose [see, for example, R. Kaiser, *Rev. Sci. Instr.*, **31**, 963 (1960)].

The rewards for successful analysis of complicated nuclear magnetic resonance spectra are considerable, and uses in assignments of chemical structures are well known. More subtle and perhaps much more valuable information may be inferred about chemical binding and electron distributions through further correlation of the magnitudes and signs of chemical shifts and coupling constants with other molecular parameters. The relative signs of coupling constants seem particularly interesting in relation to molecular structure.

* Interesting work along these lines has been reported by R. A. Hoffman and S. Gronowitz, *Arkiv. Kemi*, **15**, 45 (1959); R. A. Hoffman, *J. Chem. Phys.*, **33**, 1256 (1960); C. A. Reilly and J. D. Swalen, *J. Chem. Phys.*, **32**, 1378, **33**, 1257 (1960), and in press.

If the present status of spin-spin splitting looks confused and difficult, one can take heart in the familiar quotation from Ellis: "The Promised Land always lies on the other side of a wilderness."

112

Precession (*see* Nuclear precession)
Product wave functions, 32–35
  abbreviation of, 37

"Raising" operator, 38–39
Resonance line shapes, 6
Resonance peak areas, 5–6

Secular determinant, 52–53
Secular equations, 52
Spectral moments, 104
Spectrometer, nuclear magnetic resonance, principles of
      operation of, 4
Spin, 2
Spin decoupling, 104
Spin quantum numbers, 2
Spin-spin interaction energies, calculation of, 42–43
Spin-spin interaction operator (*see* Hamiltonian energy
      operator)
Spin-spin splitting, in A_2 systems, 30–49
  in AB systems, 49–60
  in AB_2 systems, 65–71
  in ABC systems, 85–87
  in ABX systems, 71–85
  in AMX systems, 63–65
  in AX systems, 25–30
  in AX_2 systems, 63–65
  in A_2X_2 systems, 90–101
  computer programs for calculation of, 87, 103–104
  coupling constants and structure, 9–10, 104
  effect on, of deuterium substitution, 9
  of equivalent protons, 9, 45
  in ethyl derivatives, 7, 9
  with ethyl iodide, 7
  field invariance of, 8

Spin-spin splitting, first-order, 7
    field independence of, 8–9
   line intensities in, 10
   qualitative theory of, 7–10
   qualitative theory of line multiplicities in, 9
   second-order, 7
    field dependence of, 8
Spin variable, 31
Spin wave functions, 30–33
   calculation of energy corresponding to, 31–33
   normalization of, 34
   normalized, 31
   orthogonal, 31
Stationary states, 30
Symmetric spin wave functions, 34
   of A_2 systems, 34
    calculation of energy of, 35
   of A_2X_2 systems, 97
Symmetric states, nuclear precession in, 46–49

Tetramethylsilane, as reference for chemical shifts, 6
Transition probabilities, calculation of, for A_2 systems, 38–40
   for AB systems, 58–60
   for ABX systems, 78–85
   of combination transitions, 63–64, 69
   principles involved in calculation of, 38
Transitions, allowed, 3, 26–27
   classification of, 55–56
   combination, 63–64
    of A_2B systems, 69
    of ABX systems, 75
    of AX_2 systems, 63–64
   forbidden, 26–27, 40–41, 49
    in ABX, 75
    in A_2X_2 systems, 99